A2 BIOLOGY

Revision Guide

David Applin

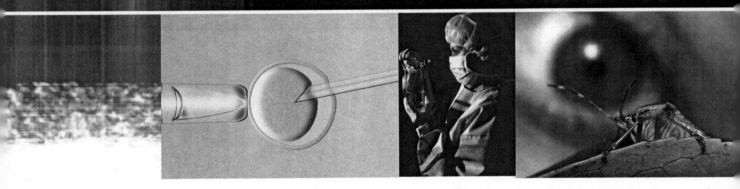

OXFORD
UNIVERSITY PRESS

Introduction

I hope that *A2 Biology for AQA Revision Guide* helps you to do well in your examinations. Although these are an important goal they are not the only reason for studying Biology. I hope also that you will develop a real and lasting interest in the living world which studying Biology will help you to understand. If you enjoy using this book then all the effort of writing it will have been worthwhile.

Getting the most out of this Revision Guide

This *Revision Guide* covers the subject content of the specification for the AQA A2 Biology award 2411 examinable from 2009. It is not intended to replace textbooks and other learning resources but rather to provide succinct coverage of all aspects of the AQA specification, A2 Biology.

It is written to be accessible to all students. You will find it useful whether you wish to continue studying Biology after A-level or want to achieve as high a grade as possible at A2, as part of a suite of qualifications suitable for continuing studies in other areas.

The *A2 Biology for AQA Revision Guide* departs from textbook style. Where appropriate, content is presented as annotated diagrams, flow charts and graphics integrated with easy-to-read text which nevertheless maintains standards of accuracy and scientific literacy which will enable you to obtain the highest grade possible in your exams. It includes the latest developments in the biological sciences.

- **Special features** – The different features of the *Revision Guide* are explained on the facing page. These will help you to get the most out of the book.

- **Revising successfully** – This gives you helpful tips on how to organize your revision, make the most of your time, and different strategies to help you recall what you have learned.

- **Assessment for A2 Biology** – This sets out the structure of the A2 Biology qualification for AQA, and marks allocated to each part of the assessment process. It will help you understand the different areas covered in the Specification and the skills you require. It also gives some helpful tips for answering questions and maximizing your marks.

- **End of unit questions and answers** – Test yourself at the end of each unit with further questions at the back of the book. A guide to the required answers is given.

Good luck with your exams!

David Applin

OXFORD

Great Clarendon Street, Oxford OX2 6DP

Oxford University Press is a department of the University of Oxford.
It furthers the University's objective of excellence in research, scholarship, and education by publishing worldwide in

Oxford   New York

Auckland   Cape Town   Dar es Salaam   Hong Kong   Karachi
Kuala Lumpur   Madrid   Melbourne   Mexico City   Nairobi
New Delhi   Shanghai   Taipei   Toronto

With offices in

Argentina   Austria   Brazil   Chile   Czech Republic   France   Greece
Guatemala   Hungary   Italy   Japan   Poland   Portugal   Singapore
South Korea   Switzerland   Thailand   Turkey   Ukraine   Vietnam

© Oxford University Press 2009

The moral rights of the author have been asserted

Database right Oxford University Press (maker)

First published 2009

Data available

ISBN 978 0 19 915271 1

10 9 8 7 6 5 4 3 2

Printed in Great Britain by Bell and Bain Ltd, Glasgow

Design and illustration by Steve Evans.

Acknowledgements

Although authors write in isolation, each book is the result of team effort. It is therefore a pleasure to acknowledge the colleagues who have contributed to this work, especially: Eileen Ramsden, author and formerly of Wolfreton School, Hull; Peter Marshall, former Head of Biology the Leys School, Cambridge; Piers Wood, tutor Mander Portman Woodward, Cambridge; John Mullins of St Ivo School, Cambridgeshire. To them all, grateful thanks for many discussions and ideas. Particular thanks are due to my editor Sarah Ware whose patience and sympathetic handling of the manuscript have ensured that this Revision Guide is student-friendly throughout and a highly effective resource for learning and revision. Finally the unstinting support of my family helped to ensure a successful conclusion to the project.

D G Applin

Cambridge, July 2009

Diagrams: p10 (right), p19, p32, p38, p72 © David Applin

Contents

Special features

As you use the *Revision Guide* you will notice different features. These will help you to focus on important points and guide your revision.

- **Objectives** at the beginning of each section list the specification content covered in the section.

- 'Before you start...' points you to other parts of the *Revision Guide* where related topics are explained.

- **Key words** are highlighted in **bold** in the text. You will find all words in the index are **bold** in the text, helping you to identify them at a glance.

- **As a result** ⓔ provides an explanation which arises from a sequence of linked facts or processes.

- 'Notice' in the text draws your attention to important facts which are illustrated in a diagram, graph, or table.

- 'Remember' prompts you to recall facts relevant to the content you're revising.

- **Fact file** provides interesting points related to specification content for you to note.

- **How science works** is an important feature of the new specifications. The concept follows on from your work at GCSE. It focuses on the processes of scientific enquiry and the implications of scientific developments for society. The *Revision Guide* provides a selection of examples which follow the criteria A–L listed in 3.7 of the specification.

- **Qs and As** offer the opportunity to ask a question and provide a model answer relevant to an aspect of the specification that might cause confusion when answering exam questions.

- **Questions** at the end of each section test your knowledge and understanding of the content of the section you're revising.

Revising successfully

To be successful in AS level Biology you must be able to:
- recall information
- apply your knowledge to new and unfamiliar situations
- carry out precise and accurate experimental work
- interpret and analyse your own experimental data and that of others

Careful revision will enable you to perform at your best in your examinations. Work with determination and tackle the course in small chunks. Make sure that you are active in your revision – just reading information is not enough.

Useful strategies for revision

As well as reading this *Revision Guide*, you might like to use some or all of the following strategies:
- Make your own condensed summary notes.
- Write key definitions onto flash cards.
- Work through facts until you can recall them.
- Ask your friends and family to test your recall.
- Make posters which cover items of the specification for your bedroom walls.
- Carry out exam practice.

Measure your revision in terms of the progress you are making rather than the length of time you have spent working. You will feel much more positive if you are able to say specific things you have achieved at the end of a day's revision rather than thinking 'I spent eight hours inside on a sunny day!' Don't sit for extended periods of time. Plan your day so that you have regular breaks, fresh air, and things to look forward to.

How to improve your recall

Here's a good strategy for recalling information:
- Focus on a small number of facts. Copy out the facts repeatedly in silence for five minutes then turn your piece of paper over and write them from memory.
- If you get any wrong then just write these out for another five minutes.

Assessment for A2 Biology

The table below shows how the marks are allocated in the AQA A2 Biology course. Notice that unit 4 has a lower mark allocation than unit 5. This is so that unit 4 may be taught in the autumn term of year 13. Students may then sit the unit 4 examination in January. Alternatively students may sit both units 4 and 5 in June.

Unit	Name of unit	Method of assessment	% of A-level exam
4	Populations and environments	Exam 1 hour 30 minutes 75 raw marks (100 UMS)	16.7
5	Control in cells and in organisms	Exam 2 hours 15 minutes 100 raw marks (140 UMS)	23.3
6	Investigative and practical skills in A2 Biology	Assessed during the course. If your work is internally marked (the Centre Marked Route) you will complete two components: • Practical skills assessment (PSA) • Investigative skills assignment (ISA) If your work is externally marked (the Externally Marked Route) you will also complete two components: • Practical skills verification (PSV) • Externally marked practical assignment (EMPA) For either route there are 50 raw marks (60 UMS).	10

- Finally test your recall of all the facts.
- Come back to the same facts later in the day and test yourself again.
- Then revisit them the next day and again later in the week.

By carrying out this process the facts will become part of your long-term memory – you will have learnt them!

Once you have built up a solid factual knowledge base you need to test it by completing some past papers for practice. It might be a good idea to tackle several questions on the same topic from a number of papers rather than working through a whole paper at once. This will enable you to identify your weak areas so that you can work on them in more detail.

Finally, remember to complete some mock exam papers under exam conditions.

Assessment Objectives

Each of these units will examine your ability to meet the assessment objectives below. Work through the statements and highlight the key words. Note that these are skills not lists of content. Full details are found in your specification or on the AQA website.

Assessment objectives one and two are assessed across all units while assessment objective three is assessed mainly in unit six.

- Assessment Objective One – Knowledge and understanding of science and of *How Science Works*
- Assessment Objective Two – Application of knowledge and understanding of science and of *How Science Works*
- Assessment Objective Three – How Science Works

Quality of Written Communication (QWC)

You should ensure that text is legible and that spelling, punctuation, and grammar are accurate so that meaning is clear, select and use a form and style of writing appropriate to purpose and to complex subject matter. Organize information clearly and coherently, using specialist vocabulary where appropriate

Quality of written communication is assessed across all units; if you write clear, well explained answers then you should obtain any marks assigned to it.

Investigative and practical skills

Your school will decide if your work is to be internally or externally marked – this has no impact on the work you will complete but does make the system appear slightly more complicated.

Answering exam papers

When you look at your exam paper read through all the questions. Identify which are the easiest for you to answer. Start by answering these questions.

Remember to read each question carefully and make sure you are answering the question that is actually set and not the one you would like to be set. Remember to look at the number of marks available for each question and tailor the number of points you make in your answer accordingly. *Do not* write an essay for a question that only attracts one or two marks!

With short-answer questions, look at the amount of space that has been left for the answer. This indicates the length of answer that the examiner anticipates you to give – depending on the size of your handwriting, of course. Make every effort to answer all the questions. An unanswered question will always score 0! If you can, leave enough time to check through your answers at the end.

Here are some popular words which are often used in exam questions. Make sure you know what the examiner means when each of these words is used.

- **Describe** – Write down all the key points using words and, where appropriate, diagrams. Think about the number of marks that are available when you write your answer.

- **Calculate** – Write down the numerical answer to the question. Remember to include your working and the units.

- **State** – Write down the answer. Remember a short answer rather than a long explanation is required.

- **Suggest** – Use your biological knowledge to answer the question. This term is used when there is more than one possible answer or when the question involves an unfamiliar context.

- **Sketch** – When this word is used a simple freehand answer is acceptable. Remember to make sure that you include any important labels.

- **Define** – Write down what a biological term or statement means.

- **Explain** – Write down a supporting argument using your biological knowledge. Think about the number of marks that are available when you write your answer.

- **List** – Write down a number of points. Think about the number of points required.

- **Discuss** – Write down details of the points in the given topic.

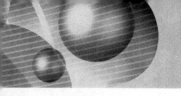

OBJECTIVES

By the end of the section you should understand the meaning of these terms and the relationship between them:

○ *Biosphere*

○ *Community*

○ *Ecosystem*

○ *Habitat*

○ *Niche*

○ *Population*

All of the places on Earth where there is life form the biosphere. Organisms are adapted (suited) to where they live. Where they live is made up of:

- an **abiotic** (non-living) environment of air/soil/water
- a **biotic** (living) **community** of animals, plants, fungi, and microorganisms.

An environment and its community form an **ecosystem** which is a more or less self-contained part of the biosphere. 'Self-contained' means that the organisms living in a particular environment are characteristic of that environment because of the adaptations that enable them to live there and not in a different ecosystem. Put simply, for example, roots anchor plants in soil; fins enable fish to swim in water.

Each type of organism (species) in an ecosystem forms a **population**. The term **ecology** refers to the relationship between populations and between populations and the environment of the ecosystem of which they are a part. The other terms listed in the Objectives (see left) refer to the different components of all the ecosystems which make up the biosphere.

The concept map shows the relationship between the terms in an oakwood ecosystem. The numbers on the concept map refer to the components of the ecosystem and are summarized in the checklist points. The organization of the components is the same for any ecosystem.

COMMUNITY ❷

Key
1 oak tree
2 hazel
3 holly
4 bluebell
5 wood anemone
6 primrose
7 moss on tree trunk
8 pigeons, rooks living in canopy
9 bluetits, woodpeckers living further down tree
10 great tits, warblers living in shrubs
11 wrens, blackbirds living on ground
12 toadstools on rotting log
13 woodlice in detritus
14 earthworm pulling leaf into burrow falling leaves

THE ECOSYSTEM

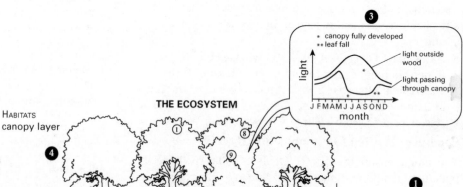

HABITATS
canopy layer

shrub layer
field layer
ground layer
detritus layer

Fact file

What are adaptations?

Adaptation refers to all of the characteristics of an organism which enable it to survive in a particular environment. Characteristics include an organism's:

- **morphology** – body structure

- **molecular biology** – the organization and function of molecules in cells

- **physiology** – the way the body works

- **biochemistry** – the chemistry of cells

- **behaviour** – an individual's reactions to changes in its environment

EXAMPLE HABITAT
Decomposers (which break down dead organic matter) at work on dead wood.

Earthworms pull dead leaves into their burrows for food.

❺ **NICHE**
Fungal hyphae decompose dead wood, releasing minerals into the environment.

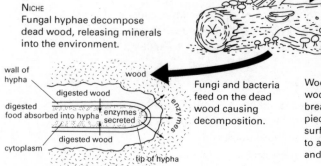

wall of hypha

wood

digested wood

digested food absorbed into hypha — enzymes secreted

enzymes

digested wood

cytoplasm

tip of hypha

Fungi and bacteria feed on the dead wood causing decomposition.

Woodlice and other wood-eating animals break up the tree into pieces increasing the surface area exposed to attack by fungi and bacteria.

Decomposition releases gases and minerals into the soil.

nutrients essential for the growth of plants

Nitrates and phosphates are absorbed in solution by the roots.

The components of an oak wood ecosystem

Checklist

1
- There is overlap where the boundaries of ecosystems meet. For example, the boundary of an oakwood is where the trees thin into grassland.
  - As a result organisms from each ecosystem may be found at the boundary.
- The exchange of organisms across the boundary is limited because the organisms are **adapted** to the particular ecosystem in which they live.
  - As a result the unique character of each ecosystem is maintained.

2
- Individuals of a particular type of organism (**species**) living in a particular place at a particular time, form a **population**. The **community** is made up of all of the different populations living in a particular ecosystem at a particular time.

3
- The **environment** is the place where a community of organisms lives.
- Different factors in the environment affect the distribution and types of organism of a community:
  - **abiotic** (physical) factors include climate, conditions of air/soil/water, characteristics of location such as altitude (the height of land above sea level) and depth of water
  - **biotic** factors include competition, predator/prey interactions, other relationships between organisms

Fact file

In 1934 the Russian biologist G F Gause stated that a niche is occupied by only **one species population** at any one time. The principle is called the **Gause hypothesis**.

- As a result competition for limited resources between different species is reduced.

- As a result niches are **separated** from each other and limited resources are shared between different species.

- As a result resources in limited supply are not over-exploited.

Fact file

The cells of most types of fungi consist of a mass of thread-like cells, forming a **mycelium**. Each thread is called a **hypha** (pl. hyphae).

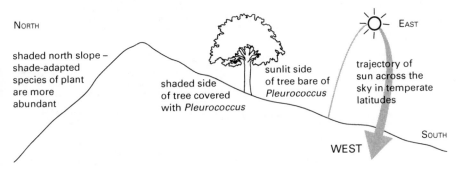

Aspect (lie of the land) is an **abiotic** factor which affects the distribution of organisms. *Pleurococcus* is a type of unicellular green alga which grows on the bark of trees. It is more abundant on the shaded north side of tree trunks than on the more brightly lit south side.

4
- The **habitat** is the localized part of the environment where a population lives and which provides most of the resources its members need.
- *Notice* that the different layers of vegetation in the oakwood provide habitats for different bird species, for example.

5
- The **niche** is the totality of all that an organism does in its habitat, including all of the resources it consumes. Resources refer to food, space, availability of mates, and other requirements which enable a species to survive in its habitat. Information about its niche tells us what a species feeds on, what feeds on it, where it rests, and how it reproduces.
  - **Fundamental niche** – all of the resources a species can exploit in theory in the absence of competition.
  - **Realized niche** – all of the resources a species can exploit in reality because of competition.
- *Notice* on the concept map the example habitat of a rotting log. Fungi and bacteria feed on the dead wood causing its decomposition. They are called **decomposers**. Their niche in the habitat breaks down dead organic matter.
  - As a result the decomposers obtain food and their activities release different compounds as gases and nutrients into the environment.
  - As a result elements (e.g. carbon and nitrogen) are recycled through the ecosystem.

Questions

1 Explain your understanding of ecology.
2 What is the difference between a habitat and niche?
3 Explain your understanding of adaptations.

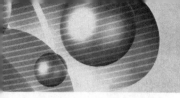

By the end of the section you should

○ *understand different methods of investigating populations*

○ *be able to consider ethical issues arising from field work*

Before you start it will help to read **4.01** (ecosystem, habitat, population).

Populations and the ecosystems where they live are usually too large for it to be practical to study everything about them. Instead **samples** are taken of the ecosystem under investigation. The samples are assumed to be representative of the ecosystem as a whole.

Fieldwork produces data which makes it possible to draw conclusions about populations and ecosystems in general. The diagram illustrates different ways of sampling

populations in the different habitats of a woodland ecosystem. Using equipment which is suitable for sampling the populations is an important choice if the fieldwork is to be successful. For example, quadrats would not be useful to sample populations of fast moving animals.

An investigation is designed so that samples are taken at **random**. Random sampling means that any part of an ecosystem (its abiotic environment/populations) has an equal chance of being sampled. Different methods are used to ensure random sampling, such as using tables of random numbers to select samples.

Random sampling avoids bias in the data gathered during an investigation. Biased data might lead to false conclusions. We can never be absolutely sure of any conclusions drawn from data. The conclusions are **tentative** (not definitive). However we can improve confidence in data by reducing error in the sampling methods used to obtain the data.

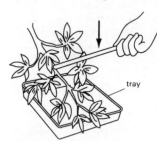

Tree beating - a stick is used to tap the branches of shrubs or trees, knocking small animals living there on to a tray or white cloth.
• do not damage the shrub or tree
• count the animals and identify them

Reducing sampling errors
• take enough samples
• take samples following a *consistent* pattern (e.g. tap branches the same number of times for each sample)
• do not sample the same branch more than once

tray

Line transect - used to map plants along a line tied between two trees, shrubs, or other suitable objects. Measure at one metre marks.
• distance to the ground
• plant species growing under the mark
• height of plant(s)

Reducing sampling errors - only record the plants growing directly under each of the one metre marks along the line of transect

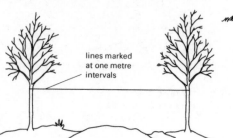

lines marked at one metre intervals

twine at 10 cm intervals

frame half a metre along each side – called a quadrat

Quadrat - a square frame used to identify and count the number of plants or animals in a *known* area.
• throw the quadrat at random in the study area
• count the plants or animals and identify them
• calculate abundance as the number of squares that the plant or animal occupies

Reducing sampling errors
• take sufficient number of samples
• avoid choosing 'good looking' areas to sample. *Remember*, sampling must be *random*
• only count individual plants or animals that lie at least half inside each square of the quadrat, to estimate their abundance

Sweep net - a strong cotton bag attached to a handle and swept through tall grass and other vegetation. 'Swishing' the net through the grass knocks small animals (e.g. insects, spiders) into the bag.
• count the animals and identify them

Reducing sampling errors:
• take a sufficient number of samples
• take samples following a *consistent* pattern (e.g. walk ten paces while 'swishing', taking one 'swish' for each step)
• do not sample the same area of vegetation more than once

Belt transect - uses quadrat and line transect together. Useful for measuring changes in vegetation between two points.
• lay down tape or rope along the line of the transect
• use a quadrat to record the plant species at intervals along the transect
• estimate abundance of each species

Reducing sampling errors
• the position of the quadrat along the line of transect should follow a *consistent* pattern

quadrat

line of transect

positions of quadrat along transect

Quadrats are not suitable for sampling mobile animals. However they are suitable for sampling small static animals (e.g. limpets clinging to the rocks by the sea shore)

Fieldwork describes what is done to gather data from ecosystems.

How science works (C)

Reducing sampling error

In general, ways of reducing error include

• random sampling
• consistent methods of working
• taking a number of samples (the more the better – within practical limits!)
• standardizing when samples are taken (e.g. at the same time of day, same season, similar weather conditions)

… all contribute to methods of field work which enable reliable data to be gathered for analysis. Data analysis leads to conclusions about the populations and ecosystems under investigation. Appropriate statistical tests of the data help to improve confidence in the conclusions drawn.

How science works (J)

Ethical issues

Fieldwork in the tree tops of tropical rainforest is a challenge. However, different methods of sampling the populations living there help scientists to collect data which is improving our understanding of biodiversity (and genetic diversity). For example, more than 30 million species of insect new to science are estimated to be living in the branches, leaves, fruits and flowers of rainforest trees – and insects are only one taxon (group) of the animal kingdom.

Methods of sampling rainforest insects fall into two general categories:

- bringing the insects to the ground where scientists collect them

- enabling scientists to reach the insects in the tree tops

For example:

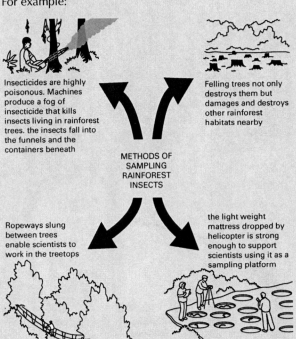

Insecticides are highly poisonous. Machines produce a fog of insecticide that kills insects living in rainforest trees. the insects fall into the funnels and the containers beneath

Felling trees not only destroys them but damages and destroys other rainforest habitats nearby

METHODS OF SAMPLING RAINFOREST INSECTS

Ropeways slung between trees enable scientists to work in the treetops

the light weight mattress dropped by helicopter is strong enough to support scientists using it as a sampling platform

The methods which bring insects to the ground destroy populations and habitats. Scientists working in the tree tops disturb the habitats of animals living there. The ethical issues arising from the fieldwork might determine which methods are used to sample rainforest insects.

Where do you think the balance lies? Make a list of *fors* and *againsts* for each of the methods of sampling rainforest insects shown in the diagram.

Estimating population size

Only by counting all the individuals of a population can an absolute figure be placed on the size of a population. This approach is only possible for individuals of **sessile** (static) species which are spread out and easily seen. For mobile species (individuals moving from place to place) different ways of estimating population size are used. One method is called the **capture/recapture** method or the **Lincoln Index** (named after the American biologist who worked it out).

How does the method work?

Imagine you want to find the size of a population of a species of snail. You need a small quantity of dull, water-based paint and a thin paintbrush (a twig will do).

- Dab a small spot of paint onto a known number of snails (not less than 40), returning each one to the spot where you found it.
- After a day or so return and collect a similar number of snails. Do not specially look out for marked snails.
- Count the number of marked snails in your second collection.

The size of the snail population is estimated as follows:

$$\text{population size} = \frac{\text{number of snails marked first time} \times \text{number of snails collected second time}}{\text{number of marked snails collected second time}}$$

How science works (D & L)

Estimating the size of a snail population using the Lincoln Index

A person collects a sample of 84 snails of a particular species from a small area of grass covered bank, marks them with a dab of paint and returns them to the place from where they were collected. A few days later the person collects a sample of 85 snails from the same area. 42 snails of this second sample are marked with a dab of paint.

Q Estimate the size of the snail population.

A *Using the Lincoln Index:*

the size of the snail population = $\dfrac{84 \times 85}{42} = 170$

Q Why is dull, water-based paint used to mark the snails?

A *Dull paint decreases the risk of marked snails being noticed by predators. Water-based paint eventually washes off and does not damage the snail.*

Q Why should you not specially look out for marked snails?

A *If marked snails are deliberately collected then the size of the snail population will be under-estimated.*

The **Qs and As** explain how conservation (in this example a particular species of snail) relies on science to inform decision-making.

Questions

1 Froghoppers (small insects) live in long grass. A sample of 90 froghoppers was collected in a field using a sweep net. Each froghopper was marked with a spot of dull water soluble paint. A second sample taken 24 hours later produced a sample of 80 froghoppers. Six were marked.

   a Estimate the population of froghoppers in the field.

   b Explain why dull water soluble paint was used to mark the froghoppers.

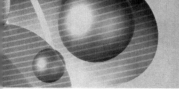
OBJECTIVES

By the end of the section you should

○ *understand that different abiotic and biotic factors affect the distribution of organisms*

○ *know the difference between intraspecific and interspecific competition*

○ *understand that intraspecific and interspecific competition have different outcomes*

Before you start it will help to read sections **4.01** (community, habitat, niche), **4.04** (population size), **4.24** (natural selection).

Adaptations to abiotic factors: an example

Why do woodlice live under stones, in layers of detritus and other dark, damp places?

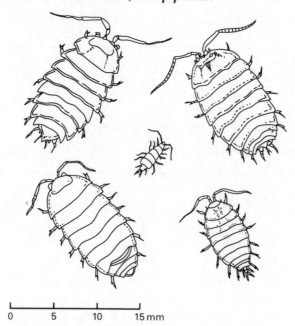

```
0        5        10       15 mm
```

European woodlice – different species are different sizes.

- *Remember* that woodlice are arthropods. The exoskeleton that encases the woodlouse body lacks the waxy waterproof layer which impregnates the exoskeleton of other arthropods such as insects and spiders.
  - Ⓔ As a result woodlice quickly lose water from the body in dry air, threatening their survival.
  - Ⓔ As a result woodlice live in dark, damp places where the air is saturated with water vapour (**humid**).
  - Ⓔ As a result loss of water from the woodlouse body is reduced.
- Damp places are an example of a **microhabitat**. They provide highly localized environments in miniature where abiotic factors may be different from the abiotic factors of the habitat as a whole.
  - Ⓔ As a result woodlice can survive where they would perish elsewhere in the habitat.

Abiotic factors affect the distribution of organisms

The term 'distribution of organisms' refers to where living things are found in an ecosystem. Abiotic factors affect the distribution of organisms. They include:

Light
The intensity of light is an important abiotic influence on the distribution of organisms inside temperate woodland (see page 6). It affects the rate of photosynthesis and therefore the amount of plant growth under the canopy layer of the trees.

- Plants of the field layer grow and flower in the spring. The plants take advantage of the increasing intensity of sunlight for photosynthesis. The sunlight reaches the woodland floor through branches bare of leaves.

Ⓔ As a result, more food and shelter are available for animals.

Rain and temperature
With rain and warmth, communities flourish. The diagram shows the effect of seasonal rainfall on the distribution of plants in West Africa. Weather stations are located at the places named on the map. Changes in the type of vegetation are shown along a transect marked A–B.

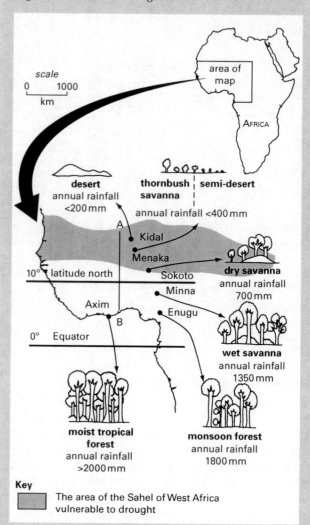

Key

�▢ The area of the Sahel of West Africa vulnerable to drought

Biotic factors affect the distribution of organisms

The biotic factors which affect the distribution of organisms include competition, predator/prey interactions, and other interactions.

Competition

In nature, living things are **competitors** (rivals) for resources which are *in limited supply*. The resources include water, food, light, space, and mates.

- **Intraspecific competition** refers to competition between individuals of the same species. For example cacti are widely spaced apart. They look as if they have been planted out in a regular arrangement. Although many tiny cactus seedlings sprout in a particular area, the pattern appears because there is only enough water for some of them to grow into mature plants. Growing cacti are the competitors and water is the resource in short supply. In particular, those cacti whose root systems develop and spread the most extensively underground absorb the most water, depriving their slower-growing rivals. The extent of each root system determines the distance between neighbouring cacti.
- **Interspecific competition** refers to competition between individuals of different species. It often leads to one species displacing another from a particular niche. For example, red squirrels (*Sciurus vulgaris*) were common in woodlands throughout Britain before the introduction of grey squirrels (*S. carolinensis*) from North America in the 1870s. Now, red squirrels are restricted to a few pockets of woodland in England although they remain fairly common in Scotland. It seems that both species compete for similar types of food but that grey squirrels are more efficient at the task. In Scotland, grey squirrels may be at the northern limits of their climate range and find it more difficult than red squirrels to survive the harsher weather.

Competition between organisms not only affects their distribution. It also has other outcomes.

Short-term outcomes:

- Intraspecific competition helps to control population size. For example the competition by cacti for water, means that slower growing plants are more likely to be affected by water shortage and therefore less likely to survive.
- Interspecific competition ensures that only one species occupies a particular niche at a particular time (the Gause hypothesis).
  - As a result available space, food, water, etc. is shared between different species.
  - As a result the number of species occupying a habitat is at a maximum (biodiversity) with respect to the environmental resources available.

Long-term outcomes:

- Intraspecific competition is a component of **natural selection**. The individuals whose characteristics best adapt them to obtain environmental resources are more likely to reproduce (because they are more likely to survive) than less well adapted individuals.

- As a result their offspring will inherit the genes responsible for the favourable characteristics.
- As a result favourable genes accumulate in the population and the species changes (**evolves**) over time.
- Interspecific competition leads to **competitive exclusion** (a species excludes another species from a particular niche).
  - As a result the displaced species becomes **extinct** unless it is able to transfer and adapt to another niche.

Predator/prey interactions

Predators attempt to catch prey. Prey attempt to escape predators. The interaction between predator and prey is intense: not least because the predator requires food and predation is fatal for the prey! The relationship affects the distribution of predators and prey. Put simply, predators gather where prey is abundant and prey will tend to avoid predators.

Other interactions

'Interaction' means the way in which a species affects another species including their respective distributions. Competition and the relationship between predator and prey are examples. Other forms of interaction include:

- **mutualism** – two or more species benefit from their close relationship. Pollination in flowering plants often depends on insects. In return, the flower's visitors benefit from the sweet-tasting nectar stored in the nectaries.
- **commensalism** – an association between one species that benefits (the commensal) and another which is unaffected either way. For example some species of fish are immune to the sting cells on the tentacles of sea anemones. Living among the tentacles means that the fish gain protection from predators. The sea anemone seems to be unaffected by the fish.
- **parasitism** – an association between one species that benefits (parasite) and another which is harmed (host). The parasite is usually much smaller than the host. Beef tapeworms live in the human intestines surrounded by digested food. They absorb food through the body wall. The host is deprived of food and the intestine may become blocked. The tapeworm's wastes cause illness.

Questions

1 What are abiotic factors?
2 Explain the difference between intraspecific competition and interspecific competition.
3 Explain the difference between an organism's habitat and its niche.

11

4.04 Population size

OBJECTIVES

By the end of the section you should

○ *be able to explain how a population may vary in size*

○ *be able to explain the effects of biotic factors*

○ *be able to explain the effects of predator-prey relationships on population size*

Before you start it will help to read sections **4.03** (biotic/abiotic factors), **4.22** (pioneer community), and **5.13** (homeostasis).

Remember that

- **populations** are each made up of a group of individuals of a particular species living in a particular place at a particular time

- **births** and **immigration** increase the size of a population

- **deaths** and **emigration** decrease the size of a population

Fact file

The density of a population is the number of individuals living in a given area (land) or volume (water) of habitat.

Biotic factors affect population size

Imagine a pioneer species colonizing a new area. Provided there are no shortages of food and few predators individuals are likely to survive and reproduce. Their numbers increase, and the population grows. The graph shows you how. It is called a **sigmoid growth curve** because it is S-shaped: sigma is the Greek for 's'. Follow the sequence of numbers on the graph.

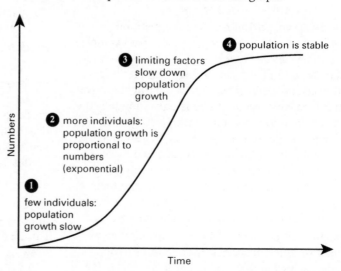

❹ population is stable

❸ limiting factors slow down population growth

❷ more individuals: population growth is proportional to numbers (exponential)

❶ few individuals: population growth slow

Numbers (y-axis) / *Time* (x-axis)

❶ To begin with the growth rate (number of individuals added to the population in a given time) is slow. This is called the **lag phase**.
Why? There are only a few individuals available for reproduction.

❷ As the number of individuals increases, the growth rate increases. This is called the **exponential phase**.

Why? More individuals are available to reproduce. However, there is little intraspecific competition for food and the effects of disease and predators are slight. Notice that the growth curve becomes steeper. At this stage the rate of increase in the population is proportional to the numbers of individuals present.

⊛ As a result the numbers of each generation is double the numbers of the previous generation. We say that population growth is geometric because the numbers of individuals of successive generations form a geometric series (e.g. 100, 200, 400, 800, 1600...)

❸ The geometric growth of a population does not continue indefinitely. As numbers build up, shortage of food, the effects of disease and predators, and other **limiting factors** such as lack of shelter and the accumulation of poisonous wastes slow the rate of growth. This is called the **phase of deceleration**.
Why? Limiting factors increase the **environmental resistance** to further population growth. The effects are **density dependent** – the more individuals there are in a particular area the greater is intraspecific competition for food, and the more likely it is that individuals will fall victims of predators and disease.

❹ Eventually, the rate of population growth levels off. This is called the **phase of stability**.
Why? The factors that add individuals to a population (births and immigration) are balanced by those that remove individuals from a population (deaths and emigration). In reality the numbers of the population fluctuate around a mean value which represents the maximum size of the population. The term **carrying capacity** refers to the level of resources of an environment able to sustain the maximum numbers of a population.

Abiotic factors affect population size

Population growth does not always follow the pattern of a sigmoid curve. For some species, populations may rapidly increase only to 'crash'. The growth curve is **J-shaped** (see right).

The steep decline in numbers is usually the result of a sudden change in abiotic conditions, for example a sharp drop in temperature. The effect is **density independent** – the 'crash' occurs regardless of the size of the population and before limiting factors begin to reduce its rate of growth.

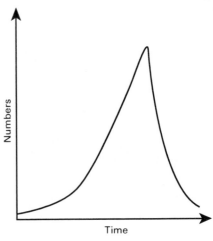

Predator and prey populations

Predators affect the numbers of their prey. Prey has an effect on the numbers of predators. If prey is scarce then some predators starve. The graph below shows the relationship between the numbers of a predator and the numbers of its prey. Follow the sequence of numbers.

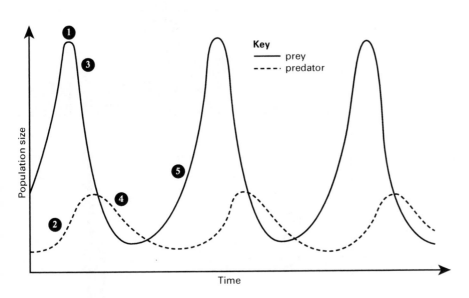

Key
— prey
---- predator

❶ Prey breed and increase in numbers if conditions are favourable (e.g. food is abundant).

❷ Predators breed and increase in numbers in response to the abundance of prey.

❸ Predation pressure increases and the number of prey declines.

❹ Predator numbers decline in response to the shortage of food.

❺ Predation pressure decreases and so prey numbers increase… and so on.

Notice that

• fluctuations in predator numbers are less than fluctuations in prey numbers
• fluctuations in predator numbers lag behind fluctuations in prey numbers
Why is this? There are fewer predators than prey, and predators tend to reproduce more slowly than prey.

Notice also that changes in the numbers of each population are density dependent.

• When the numbers of prey increase so too do the numbers of its predator, until the deaths of prey from predation exceed the number of new individuals entering the prey population through births.
  As a result the numbers of prey decrease, followed by a decrease in the number of predators, because of the lack of food. The effect is density dependent and an example of negative feedback returning a change of state (in this case, numbers of predator and prey) to a normal value (homeostasis).

Questions

1 How does a sigmoid growth curve of a population describe the increase in its numbers?

2 Give the meaning of the phrase 'density dependent'.

3 Explain why fluctuations in numbers of predator lag behind that of its prey.

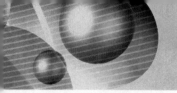
About 6.7 billion (thousand million) people live in the world today. The figure may be more than 10 billion before the end of the 21st century.

Notice:

* Numbers of the populations of **developed** countries (Japan, the countries of Europe and North America) are leveling off.

* Numbers of the populations of **developing** countries (some of the countries of South-East Asia, Africa and Latin America) are growing rapidly. Despite many deaths in developing countries from the spread of HIV/AIDS, malaria and tuberculosis, the trend worldwide is upwards.

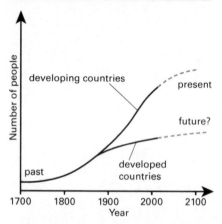

Growth curve of the human population over the past 300 years. The dotted lines show possible future growth curves.

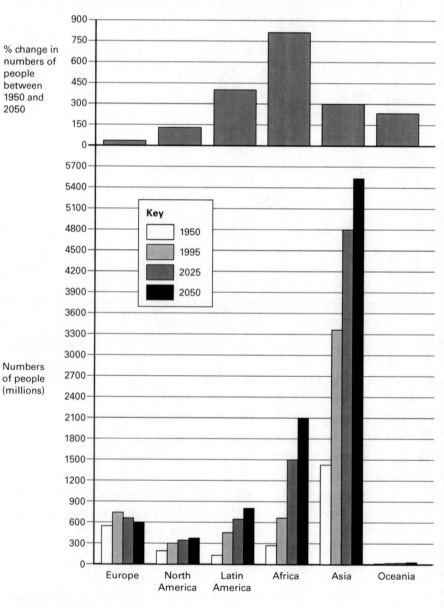

Where in the world human populations are growing
Source: UN Population Division

Fact file

'Developed' and 'developing' usually refer to economies and the literacy rates, life expectancy and poverty rates of the people.

* The economies of developed countries are complex and supported by money markets that deal worldwide in goods and natural resources. The majority of people are literate and have a long life expectancy. Absolute poverty is rare.

* The economies of developing countries may depend on a limited set of commodities (coffee, tea, cotton for example). They may be affected by the rise and fall of world markets more severely than the economies of developed countries. Life is short and poverty stricken for the majority. Literacy rates are low.

'Developing' may also refer to countries with fast growing economies but where literacy rates are relatively low. Poverty may be widespread and life expectancy depends on income. China and India are examples.

Worldwide, the rate of human population growth is affected by the number of young people in the population, particularly women of child-bearing age. Young people are a larger proportion of the population of many developing countries than of developed countries.

How science works (A)

Population growth

Remember the idea of rates:

$$\text{rate} = \frac{\text{change}}{\text{time}}$$

Therefore, for a limited period of time:

$$\text{population growth rate} = \frac{\substack{\text{population at} \\ \text{end of period}} - \substack{\text{population at} \\ \text{beginning of period}}}{\substack{\text{population at} \\ \text{beginning of period}}}$$

or ...

$$\text{population growth rate} = \frac{\text{increase in number of individuals}}{\text{time}}$$

Let:

Δ denote change in...

N = the number of individuals of a population

t = time

Therefore:

$$\frac{\text{population}}{\text{growth rate}} = \frac{\Delta N}{\Delta t}$$

Let:

α denote *proportional* to...

Therefore population growth rate at its maximum is: $\dfrac{\Delta N}{\Delta t} \, \alpha \, N$

In the absence of limiting factors (e.g. food shortages), then population growth rate depends on the number of offspring produced by each female of the population (the **intrinsic rate of increase**).

Let:

r = the intrinsic rate of increase

Therefore population growth rate is: $\dfrac{\Delta N}{\Delta t} = rN$

where the intrinsic rate of increase (r) refers to the **biotic potential** of the population. r depends on the time taken for a fertilized egg to develop into a fully formed offspring. The period of time is called the **gestation period** which for human females is approximately 9 months.

The intrinsic rate of increase (r) is calculated from the birth rate (b) and the death rate (d):

$$r = b - d$$

- Birth rate is expressed as number of births per 1000 of population per year.

- Death rate is expressed as number of deaths per 1000 of population per year.

- Currently in the USA:

    > $b = 14$

    > $d = 8$

As a result

$$r = 14 - 8 = \text{per 1000 of population} = 0.006$$

or...

$$r = 0.6\%$$

The equations and example show you how to explain and calculate population growth rate from data on birth rates and death rates.

Fact file

A country's population growth rate is affected not just by the age structure of the population but also by the average number of children each woman has during her lifetime. This is the **total fertility rate (TFR)**.

In theory, when TFR = 2 each pair of parents replaces itself. However, in practice a TFR value between 2.1 and 2.2 is needed to replace each generation – the value is the replacement rate. It is more than 2 because some women will have more children, some fewer, and some no children at all.

Questions

1 How would you describe the differences between so-called developing and developed countries?

2 What is the meaning of the term biotic potential?

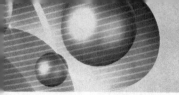

OBJECTIVES

By the end of the section you should

○ be able to interpret population growth curves, survival curves and age pyramids

○ understand the meaning of 'demographic transition'

Before you start it will help to read section **4.05** (human population growth).

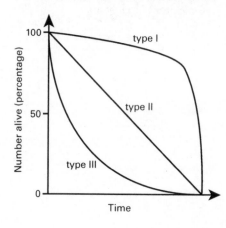

A survival curve represents the percentage of a population surviving according to age categories. There are three types:

- *type I* where most deaths occur among older individuals
- *type II* where the death rate is constant across all age categories
- *type III* where most deaths occur among younger individuals

Human populations in developed countries have a type 1 curve; most bird populations are type 2; fish and insect populations are type 3.

Notice:

- At age 0, the type I curve shows that there is 100% (more or less) survival.
- The percentage survival decreases with age as different causes of mortality remove individuals from the population.
- The type I curve bows to the right showing improved survival
  ⊛ as a result of improved
    ○ living conditions
    ○ medical technology

If we disregard immigration and emigration, birth rate (b) and death rate (d) determine changes in population size.

When: $$b = d$$

then: $$\text{change in population size} = 0$$

Information about deaths of humans can be collected and organized into a life table. The example shows you the idea.

X	I		D		M	
Age group (years)	**Numbers**		**Numbers who die**		**Mortality rate**	
	Male	**Female**	**Male**	**Female**	**Male**	**Female**
0–9	464	433	28	14	.060	.032
10–19	436	419	12	16	.027	.038
20–29	424	403	21	28	.049	.069
80–89	65	89	55	81	.840	.910
90–99	10	8	10	8	1.0	1.0
100+						

- Subtracting D from I gives the survivors for a particular age group X:

$$SX = DX - IX$$

Calculating the % survivors for each age group…

$$\% \text{ survivors} = \frac{DX - IX}{IX} \times \frac{100}{1}$$

… enables you to draw the survival curves (one for males; the other for females) of the population. Plotting both curves on the same axes enables the survival of males and females to be compared.

Notice:

- Subtracting DX from IX gives the value for I of the next age group… and so on down the table:

$$IX - DX = IX_{+1}$$

- Dividing the number of deaths (D) by the number of individuals (I) in each age group gives the mortality rate for the age group:

$$M = \frac{D}{I}$$

Questions

Refer to the diagram of age population pyramids for India and France (page 17), and explain your answers.

1 Which country has more children below the age of 5 years?

2 Which country has more people over the age of 80 years?

3 Which country has

   a the higher birth rate

   b the lower death rate?

Age

The rate of population growth is affected by the number of young people in the population, particularly women of child-bearing age. **Age population pyramids** illustrate the point.

Notice:

- The base of the pyramids represents the % of children in each country's population.
- The top of the pyramids represents the % of each country's oldest inhabitants.
- The % of all other age groups are represented in five-year steps in between.
  - Ⓔ As a result each pyramid shows the % of different age groups that makes up each country's total population.

Notice also:

- Males are figured on the left; females to the right.
- The proportion of males and females in the older age groups of a country's population is different.

Countries with broad-based pyramids like India's have populations with

- high birth rates
- low life expectancy (the majority die before reaching old age)
- improving medical technology and public health systems which reduces childhood mortality
  - Ⓔ As a result more children will survive to be adults who will have their own children.
  - Ⓔ As a result the populations will continue to grow in the foreseeable future.

Countries with narrow base pyramids like France's have populations with

- low birth rates (proportionately there are fewer women of child bearing age)
- high life expectancy (the majority survive to old age), because of well developed medical technology and public health systems
  - Ⓔ As a result populations are stable and may even decline unless immigration compensates.

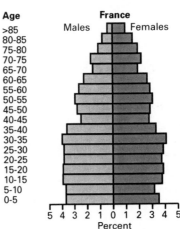

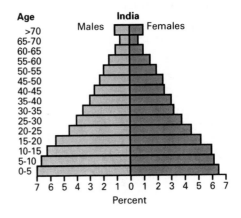

How science works (G)

Demographic transition

The economic development of a country from a pre-industrial to industrial economy is part of the meaning of 'developing' and 'developed' countries. The shift from high birth rates and death rates to low birth rates and death rates is another part of the meaning. The shift is called the **demographic transition**. Four (possibly five) stages have been identified. Age population pyramids illustrate the point.

Notice that decline in the birth rate and death rate during the demographic transition alters the age structure of populations.

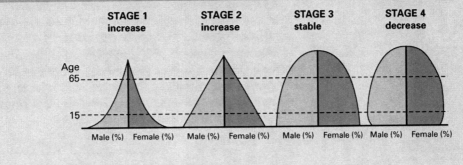

	STAGE 1 increase	STAGE 2 increase	STAGE 3 stable	STAGE 4 decrease
Economy:	pre-industrial	developing	industrial	post-industrial
Birth rate:	high	high	declining	low
Death rate:	high	declining	low	low
Life expectancy:	short	slightly longer	longer	even longer

Causes: Improvements in
- agriculture
- access to technology
- healthcare
- basic education
... result in declining death rates and increasing birth rates.

Increase in
- contraception
- wages
- urbanization
- status and education for women
- education improvements
- social change
and reduction in
- child labour
- subsistence agriculture
... result in declining birth rates.

17

4.07 ATP

OBJECTIVES

By the end of the section you should

○ *understand that ATP is the immediate source of energy for different biological processes in prokaryotic and eukaryotic cells*

○ *know that ATP is produced during photosynthesis and cellular respiration*

Before you start it will help to read sections **4.08** (photosynthesis) and **4.13** (cellular respiration).

ATP is short for **adenosine triphosphate**. Its molecule consists of the sugar **ribose** to which is attached the base **adenine** and a chain of three **phosphate** groups. The combination of ribose and adenine forms the **adenosine** part of the molecule.

ATP is formed when a phosphate group (Pi) binds to a molecule of **ADP** (adenosine diphosphate).

The reaction is:

- **a phosphorylation** – a type of reaction where a phosphate group is added to another molecule
- **endothermic** – a type of reaction which absorbs energy
- catalysed by the enzyme ATP **synthase**

The energy driving the synthesis of ATP comes from:

- *light* in the light-dependent reactions of photosynthesis
- *sugars* (also lipids and proteins) which are oxidized in the reactions of cellular respiration

In each case the energy released is coupled with the phosphorylation of ADP, producing ATP.

Releasing energy from ATP

ATP is an immediate source of energy for biological processes. It is very soluble in water and often described as the *universal energy currency* found in the cells of all living organisms... from bacteria to oak trees to humans.

When a molecule of ATP combines with a water molecule, the bond binding the endmost phosphate group to the rest of the ATP molecule is broken. The reaction is a **hydrolysis**. During the reaction energy is consumed breaking the bond, but more energy is released as other bonds are formed. Overall the reaction is therefore **exothermic**.

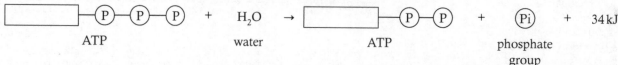

The hydrolysis of ATP is also catalysed by ATP synthase. This time the enzyme works in reverse to its activity catalysing the production of ATP. The energy released is coupled to and drives other biological processes including:

- **anabolic reactions** which result in the synthesis of **polymers** from building block units, for example monosaccharides → polysaccharides
- **active transport** of substances against their concentration gradients across cell membranes, for example
  - the transfer of glucose from blood to liver cells
  - the exchange of sodium ions (Na^+) and potassium ions (K^+) across the membrane of the axon of a nerve cell, generating an action potential
- **muscle contraction** during which muscle fibres shorten

A proportion of the energy from the hydrolysis of ATP is released as heat energy. In birds and mammals some of the heat helps to maintain a constant body temperature. The rest is transferred to the environment.

Questions

1 Name two sources of energy that drive the synthesis of ATP.

2 Why is adenosine triphosphate so-named?

3 Explain why the synthesis of ATP is described as an endothermic reaction.

OBJECTIVES

By the end of the section you should

○ *understand that photosynthesis refers to the linked reactions which convert light energy into the bond energy of triose sugar*

○ *be able to interpret the relationship between the reactions of photosynthesis and the structure of a chloroplast*

○ *be able to recall the adaptations of a leaf and its tissues which maximize the rate of photosynthesis*

Before you start it will help to read sections **4.09** (light harvesting), **4.10** (light-dependent reactions), and **4.11** (light-independent reactions)

Plants fix carbon dioxide and water, forming triose sugar. Light is the source of energy which drives the reactions. The reactions are the components of **photosynthesis**. It is a reduction process in which carbon dioxide is reduced by hydrogen derived from water. The sequence of events is shown in the diagram. *Notice* the different stages:

• **Light harvesting** – light energy is captured by chlorophyll and other light absorbing pigments

• **Light-dependent reactions** – captured light energy
   ○ splits water into hydrogen ions (H^+) and oxygen: the process is called **photolysis**
   ○ is converted into the bond energy of ATP: the process is called **photophosphorylation**

• **Light-independent reactions** – hydrogen ions (H^+) released by photolysis combine with carbon dioxide, reducing it. Triose sugar is formed.

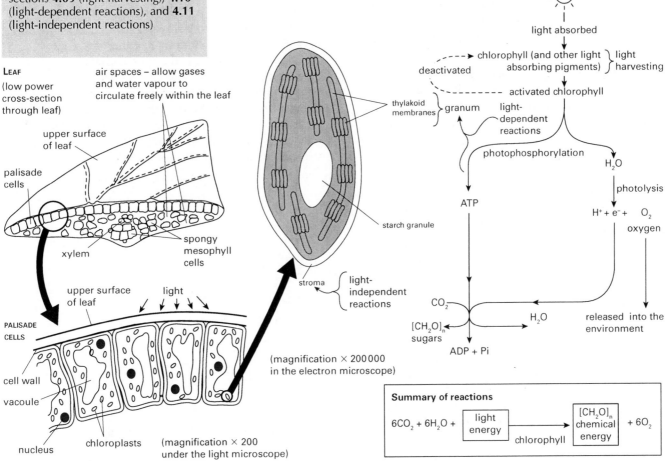

Summary of reactions

$6CO_2 + 6H_2O +$ [light energy] $\xrightarrow{\text{chlorophyll}}$ [$[CH_2O]_n$ chemical energy] $+ 6O_2$

Leaf cells and chloroplasts. Chlorophyll and other light-absorbing pigments cover the thylakoid membranes of each granum. Their large surface area maximizes the capture of light. The light-dependent reactions occur on the thylakoid membranes; the light-independent reactions occur in the stroma.

Recall the adaptations of a leaf which maximize the rate of photosynthesis. The diagram reminds you of the structure of a leaf and its tissues.

• Palisade cells beneath the upper surface of the leaf form the major photosynthetic tissue of most plants.

• Chloroplasts stream in the cytoplasm of palisade cells to the region where light is brightest. The process is called **cyclosis**.

• The elongated shape of palisade cells enables them to act as light tubes, transmitting light to tissues deep within the leaf.

• Spaces in the leaf tissue enable carbon dioxide and water vapour (the raw materials of photosynthesis) to circulate freely within the leaf.

Questions

1 Summarize the different stages of photosynthesis.

2 Explain how the structure of a chloroplast maximizes the rate of photosynthesis.

Chlorophyll and other pigments

A pigment is a substance that absorbs light. Chlorophyll is a pigment. It absorbs light of all colours (wavelengths) except green, which is mostly reflected. It is not a single compound but a mixture of several.

- **Chlorophyll** a – the **primary** pigment of photosynthesis, so called because it is directly responsible for the conversion of light energy to the bond energy of ATP. The diagram shows its structure.

chlorophyll *a*   chlorophyll *b*

Key

C·········· = long hydrocarbon tail

- ○ *Notice* that the 'head' of the molecule consists of a magnesium ion held in a ring system called a **porphyrin ring**. The structure is similar to that of haem, except that a magnesium ion substitutes for an iron ion.
- ○ *Notice* that a long hydrocarbon 'tail' is attached to the ring. The 'tail' is part of the thylakoid membrane of the chloroplast; the 'head' lies on its surface.
- ○ *Notice* the alternate double and single bonds of the porphyrin ring. When illuminated, the bonds switch back and forth as singles and doubles conducting electrons. We say that chlorophyll is **photoexcitable**.

- **Chlorophyll** b – differs from chlorophyll a in that an aldehyde group (–CHO) replaces the methyl group (–CH₃) in the position marked * on the porphyrin ring illustrated. It is an **accessory** pigment, so called because it transfers energy (photoexcited electrons) to chlorophyll *a*.

- **Carotenoids** – a group of compounds which are also **accessory** pigments. There are two categories: *carotenes* which are derived from vitamin A, and xanthophylls.

Carotenoids range in colour from pale yellow, orange, to deep red and are responsible for the colours of many fruits and flowers.

The accessory pigments absorb light at wavelengths different from those absorbed by chlorophyll *a*.

- ⓔ As a result the energy of most of the spectrum of visible light blue → red is made available for photosynthesis.

Each photosynthetic pigment absorbs particular wavelengths of light. The band of wavelengths is the **absorption spectrum** of the pigment. The **action spectrum** is a measure of how effective different wavelengths of light are in bringing about biological processes – in this case photosynthesis.

The graphs illustrate the absorption spectra for different photosynthetic pigments and the action spectrum for photosynthesis. *Notice* the close correlation between the absorption spectrum for each of the photosynthetic pigments and the action spectrum for the rate of photosynthesis by the plant as a whole. The correspondence between the two spectra is evidence that the photosynthetic performance of the plant is related to the wavelengths of light absorbed by the pigments.

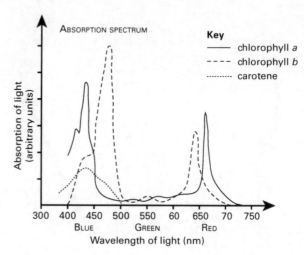

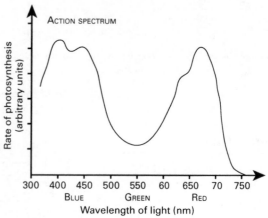

Absorption spectra for different plant pigments and the action spectrum for photosynthesis

Light harvesting

Recall that primary chlorophyll and accessory photosynthetic pigments are part of the thylakoid membranes. They are packed into units called **photosystems**. Each unit contains between 250 and 400 molecules of pigment and traps photons of light energy. *Recall* also the difference between primary and accessory photosynthetic pigments. Once absorbed by a molecule of one of the accessory pigments, a photon passes between the other accessory pigment molecules. Eventually it transfers to and is absorbed by a molecule of a special form of chlorophyll *a* – the primary pigment. The molecule is called the **reaction centre chlorophyll molecule**. It is the **reaction centre** of the photosystem. The diagram shows you the idea.

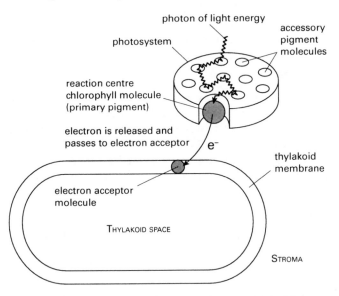

An antenna complex absorbing photons. The process is called **light harvesting**. It involves numerous pigment molecules for each photon absorbed.

When a reaction centre chlorophyll molecule absorbs a photon, the photon's energy excites an electron.

- As a result the energy level of the electron is raised.
- As a result the electron is released and transfers to a primary electron acceptor (electron acceptor 1 – see diagram page 22).
- As a result the chlorophyll molecule is oxidized and positively charged.

What happens next? Reading on will help you to answer the question.

Fact file

Like the electron transport chain of the inner mitochondrial membrane, the electron transport chain linking the primary electron acceptor 1 to photosystem 1 (PSI – see diagram page 22) consists of different proteins which transfer electrons along the chain in a series of redox reactions.

- Energy released by the redox reactions enables protons to be removed from the chloroplast stroma across the thylakoid membrane into the space enclosed by the membrane.

- As a result protons accumulate in the thylakoid space.

- As a result a proton gradient develops across the thylakoid membrane.

- Protons accumulated in the thykaloid space flow down the proton gradient (chemiosmosis) from the space through channel proteins and ATP synthase to the stroma.

- As a result energy is released.

- As a result ADP combines with Pi. The reaction is catalysed by ATP synthase. ATP is formed.

Questions

1 Why is chlorophyll called a pigment?
2 What is the difference between the absorption spectrum and action spectrum of a pigment?
3 Briefly describe the functional relationship between the different photosynthetic pigments of a photosystem.

OBJECTIVES

By the end of the section you should

○ *know that the energy from photoexcited electrons generates ATP and reduced NADP*

○ *understand that the production of ATP involves electron transfer associated with the electron transport chain in chloroplast membranes*

○ *know that the photolysis of water produces protons, electrons and oxygen*

Before you start it will help to read sections **4.07** (ATP), **4.08** (photosynthesis), **4.09** (light harvesting), and **4.16** (electron transport chain).

There are two different photosystems, each containing a slightly different version of the reaction centre chlorophyll molecule from the other:

- **photosystem I (PSI)** in which the peak absorption spectrum of the reaction centre chlorophyll molecule is 700 nm (P_{700})
- **photosystem II (PSII)** in which the peak absorption spectrum of the reaction centre chlorophyll molecule is 680 nm (P_{680})

The two systems require light and work together at the same time. The diagram and its checklist is your guide to the details of the light-dependent reactions.

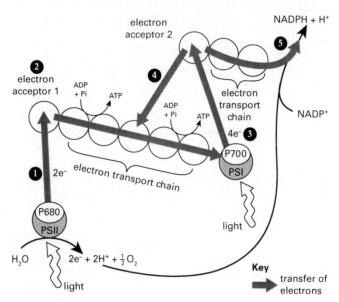

Light-dependent reactions of photosynthesis

Stage ❶

Photons of light energy are harvested by PSII and trapped by P_{680} forming the reaction centre of the photosystem. Its electrons are raised to a higher energy level, released and captured by electron acceptor 1. Now oxidized, the loss of electrons by the P_{680} of the reaction centre is repaid by electrons gained from the photolysis of water. *Remember* that photolysis also produces protons (H^+) and that oxygen gas is released.

Stage ❷

Electrons transfer from electron acceptor 1 along an electron transport chain to PSI. The transfer of electrons is by a series of redox reactions similar to that of the electron transport chain of the inner mitochondrial membrane. Energy is released enabling ADP and inorganic phosphate (Pi) to combine, forming ATP. Light energy has therefore been converted to and stored as chemical bond energy in molecules of ATP. The process is called **non-cyclic photophosphorylation** as its reactions follow a linear metabolic pathway.

Stage ❸

Photons of light energy are harvested by PSI and trapped by P_{700} forming the reaction centre of photosystem. Its electrons are raised to a higher energy level. The electrons are released and captured by electron acceptor 2. Now oxidized, the loss of electrons by the P_{700} of the reaction centre is repaid by electrons gained from the chain of electron carriers described in Stage 2.

Stage ❹

Some electrons from electron acceptor 2 pass back to PSI by the chain of electron carriers described in Stage 2. Another molecule of ATP is generated. Because electrons are recycled the process is called **cyclic photophosphorylation**.

Stage ❺

Electrons transfer from electron acceptor 2 along a chain of electron carriers to **nicotinamide adenine dinucleotide phosphate (NADP)**. They combine with the protons (H^+) released by photolysis (see Stage 1) and NADP is reduced to NADPH.

Questions

1 What is the difference between non-cyclic photophosphorylation and cyclic phosphorylation?

2 What are the sources of electrons transferred to electron acceptor 1 and electron acceptor 2?

3 How is photosystem I different from photosystem II?

OBJECTIVES

By the end of the section you should

○ *know that carbon dioxide is accepted by ribulose bisphosphate (RuBP), forming two molecules of glycerate 3-phosphate (GP)*

○ *ATP and reduced NADP are required for the reduction of GP to triose phosphate (glyceraldehyde 3-phosphate)*

○ *RuBP is regenerated in the Calvin cycle*

○ *triose phosphate is converted into useful organic substances*

Before you start it will be helpful to read sections **4.08** (photosynthesis), **4.13** (intermediate compounds), and **4.14** (phosphorylated triose sugar).

Qs and As

Q What are the biochemical outcomes of the light-dependent reactions?

A • *Light energy is converted into chemical energy.*

• *The photolysis of water releases protons (H^+), electrons (e^-), and oxygen gas.*

• *ATP and NADPH + H^+ are produced and available in the light-independent reactions where carbon dioxide is reduced, forming triose sugar.*

The **light-independent** reactions of photosynthesis take place in the stroma of chloroplasts. They occur whether or not light is available. The sequence of reactions is sometimes called the **Calvin cycle**. Like the Krebs cycle, the end product of the reactions regenerates the starting substance of the process. The diagram and its checklist is your guide to the details of the light-independent reactions.

Stage ❶

Carbon dioxide in solution diffuses through the plasma membrane, through the cytoplasm and through the membrane surrounding the chloroplasts of photosynthetic cells. In the stroma it combines with the 5-carbon compound **ribulose bisphosphate (RuBP)**, producing an unstable 6-carbon molecule which immediately splits into two 3-carbon compound molecules of **glycerate-3-phosphate (GP)**. The reaction is catalysed by the enzyme **ribulose bisphosphate carboxylate oxygenase (rubisco)** which is located on the surface of the thylakoid membranes.

Stage ❷

GP is reduced to **glyceraldehyde 3-phosphate (GALP)**, by NADPH produced in the light-dependent reactions. GALP is a phosphorylated triose sugar. The reaction is endothermic and driven by the ATP produced during photophosphorylation. $NADP^+$ is regenerated and is available to accept more protons (H^+) released by photolysis during the light-dependent reactions.

Stage ❸

The combination of two molecule of GALP produces a molecule of glucose (a 6-carbon sugar). The process is a reversal of glycolysis. The combination of many glucose molecules forms starch.

Stage ❹

Other molecules of GALP combine in a variety of reactions, regenerating RuBP. Overall 5 molecules of GALP → 3 molecules of RuBP. The process uses ATP produced by photophosphorylation during the light-dependent reactions.

Products of photosynthesis

All plant cells use sugar, including GALP and glucose, as the starting point for the synthesis of other carbohydrates and lipids. The addition of nitrogen forms amino acids and therefore proteins, as well as other nitrogen containing compounds. These different syntheses are endothermic and are driven by the ATP produced by cellular respiration.

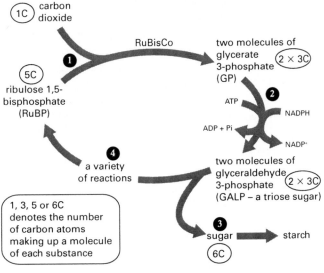

The light-independent reactions of photosynthesis

Questions

1 How is nicotinamide adenine dinucleotide phosphate (NADP) regenerated in the light-independent reactions?

2 What is meant by the statement that 'the combination of two molecules of GALP produces a molecule of glucose by reverse glycolysis'? Reference to **4.14** will help you to answer the question.

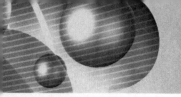

OBJECTIVES

By the end of the section you should

○ *understand the principle of limiting factors*

○ *understand how knowledge of limiting factors is applied in commercial greenhouses*

Before you start it will help to read sections **4.08** (photosynthesis), **4.10** (light-dependent reactions), **4.11** (light-independent reactions), and **4.21** (greenhouse effect).

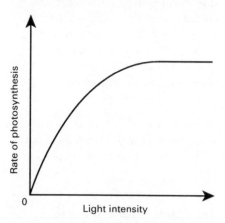

To begin with, the increase in the rate of photosynthesis is proportional to the increase in light intensity.

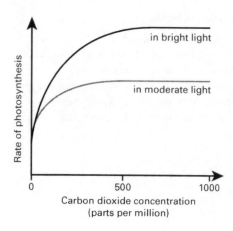

Carbon dioxide is a limiting factor

The rate of photosynthesis determines the mass of triose sugar produced in a given time. It is affected by supplies of **carbon dioxide** and **water, temperature** and the **intensity of light**. These factors are called **limiting factors** because if any one of them falls to a low level the rate of photosynthesis slows or stops – even if the other factors are in abundant supply. The greater the rate of photosynthesis the greater is the growth rate of plants. Therefore, if limiting factors slow the rate of photosynthesis then the growth rate of the plants affected also slows.

Light intensity and concentration of carbon dioxide

At constant temperature the rate of photosynthesis varies with the intensity of light. The top graph illustrates the relationship. For example:

- As dawn lightens the night sky, photosynthesis begins. *Notice* that the increase in the rate of photosynthesis is proportional to the increase in light intensity through the early morning. Light intensity is the limiting factor.
- As the intensity of light continues to increase, so too does the rate of photosynthesis. However the relationship is no longer directly proportional. Light is still a limiting factor but some other factor is limiting as well.
- Yet further increase in light intensity does *not* lead to further increase in the rate of photosynthesis. Light **saturation** is reached and the intensity of light is no longer a limiting factor. Some other factor is limiting the process.

Since temperature is constant, the 'other' limiting factor is carbon dioxide. The second graph makes the point.

- A low concentration of carbon dioxide limits the rate of photosynthesis whatever the light intensity. As the concentration of carbon dioxide increases, there is a proportional increase in the rate of photosynthesis.
- As the concentration of carbon dioxide continues to increase, so too does the rate of photosynthesis. However the relationship is no longer directly proportional. The concentration of carbon dioxide is still a limiting factor, but some other factor is limiting as well.
- Yet further increase in the concentration of carbon dioxide does not lead to further increase in the rate of photosynthesis and the concentration of carbon dioxide is no longer a limiting factor. Notice that at higher concentrations of carbon dioxide the rate of photosynthesis increases with increasing light intensity and then levels off. Now light intensity is the limiting factor.

Temperature

When light intensity is not limiting (high intensity), the rate of photosynthesis increases proportionately as temperature increases... over a limited range. However when light intensity is limiting (low intensity), the rate of photosynthesis does not increase with an increase in temperature. Why?

Remember that the process of photosynthesis consists of two stages: light-dependent and light-independent. The light-dependent reactions are **photochemical**. Most photochemical reactions are not temperature sensitive. However the enzyme catalysed reactions of the light-independent reactions are. So, increase in temperature increases the rate of photosynthesis to the point when temperature is no longer a limiting factor. Conditions are optimal for enzyme activity.

Compensation point

At night photosynthesis stops, so plants do not consume carbon dioxide but produce it because their cells continue to respire. At dawn photosynthesis begins, and some of the carbon dioxide produced through respiration is consumed. Less carbon dioxide therefore is released into the environment.

As light intensity increases, so too does the rate of photosynthesis, and less and less carbon dioxide is released. A point is reached where the carbon dioxide used by photosynthesis is balanced by the carbon dioxide produced by aerobic respiration. The *status quo* is called the **compensation point**.

Plants that grow in unshaded sunny habitats (**sun plants**) have a high compensation point. Buttercups are an example. For plants that flourish under the canopy of trees and other shaded habitats (**shade plants**) the compensation point is lower. Dogs' mercury and ivy are examples.

Notice in the graphs that the rate of photosynthesis of shade plants is maximal at a lower light intensity than for sun plants. Shade plants therefore would outgrow sun plants in shaded habitats. However, the maximum rate of photosynthesis for sun plants is greater than shade plants. Sun plants therefore would outgrow shade plants in sunny habitats.

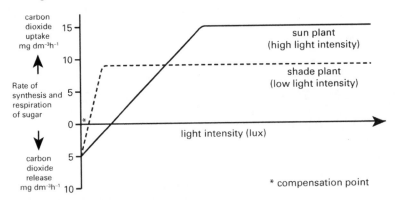

Greenhouses eliminate limiting factors

A greenhouse provides everything plants need for photosynthesis. Conditions are controlled so that the rate of photosynthesis is at a maximum.

The environment inside the greenhouse can be precisely controlled. Sensors linked to computers can monitor light intensity, temperature, moisture, and the concentration of carbon dioxide in the air. The computers process the information and alter the controls to provide optimal growing conditions for the plants.

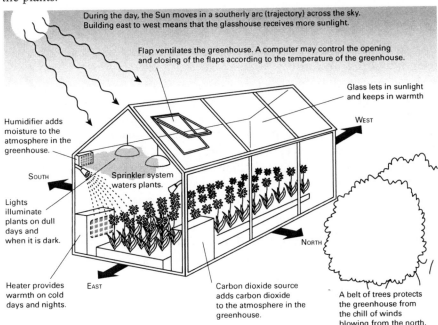

Plants grow quickly under glass because the greenhouse environment maximizes their rate of photosynthesis.

Remember that carbon dioxide is:

- *consumed* during photosynthesis
- *produced* during aerobic respiration

Fact file

Why are limiting factors limiting?

- When carbon dioxide is in short supply, the rate of conversion of RuBP to GP in the light-independent reactions decreases.

- As a result RuBP builds up and triose sugar is not produced.

- At low temperature, the number of collisions between enzyme/substrate molecules decreases.

- As a result the rate of the enzyme-catalysed reactions producing triose sugar during the light-independent reactions decreases.

- At low light intensity, the production of ATP and NADPH in the light-dependent reactions decreases (stops).

- As a result GP is not converted into triose sugar during the light-independent reactions.

- As a result GP builds up and RuBP is used up.

These effects of limiting factors reduce the rate of photosynthesis and therefore slow the rate of plant growth.

Questions

1 What is the compensation point?

2 Define a limiting factor.

3 Briefly discuss why greenhouses help to eliminate limiting factors.

Key words

Oxidation – a reaction in which a substance gains oxygen atoms or loses hydrogen atoms or electrons.

Reduction – a reaction in which a substance loses oxygen atoms or gains hydrogen atoms of electrons.

Electron – a particle with a negative charge that orbits the nucleus of an atom.

Coenzyme – a molecule which binds to an atom (or group of atoms) of one molecule and transfers the atom (or group of atoms) to another molecule.

Fact file

The term **metabolism** refers to all of the chemical reactions taking place in a cell.

- **Catabolic** reactions break down large molecules into smaller ones. The reactions of cellular respiration are an example.

- **Anabolic** reactions make (synthesize) large molecules from smaller ones. The synthesis of polysaccharides, lipids, and proteins are examples.

A metabolic pathway is a sequence (particular order) of reactions where a particular molecule is converted into another different one by way of a series of intermediate compounds.

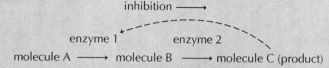

molecule A ⟶ molecule B ⟶ molecule C ⟶ molecule D ⟶ molecule E

Only small amounts of energy are released or taken in during the reaction. Cells are therefore not damaged. Reactions which require or release large amounts of energy would destroy cells.

Remember that a substance which an enzyme enables to react is called a **substrate**. The substance produced as a result of the reaction is the **product**.

If the product of one reaction of a metabolic pathway inhibits one of the enzymes preceding its formation, the product will act as an inhibitor of the whole pathway. The process is called **end-point inhibition**.

inhibition ⟶

enzyme 1   enzyme 2

molecule A ⟶ molecule B ⟶ molecule C (product)

For example molecule C inhibits enzyme 1. The metabolic pathway as a whole therefore slows down or stops. End-point inhibition is an example of negative feedback – the mechanism of homeostasis. It controls the rates of reaction of a metabolic pathway.

When glucose is oxidized completely in the presence of oxygen, the products are carbon dioxide and water. Energy is released. Overall the equation is

$$C_6H_{12}O_6(aq) + 6O_2(g) \rightarrow 6CO_2(g) + 6H_2O(l) \quad \Delta H_R -2880 \text{ kJ}$$

...where ΔH_R represents the energy change of the reaction at standard temperature and pressure.

If the energy change of the reaction were released all at once in cells, then the increase in temperature would destroy them. Instead, the energy is released step-by-step in a series of reactions in four stages: **glycolysis**, the **link reaction**, the **Krebs cycle**, and the **electron transport chain**.

Aerobic respiration refers to the link reaction, the Krebs cycle and the reactions of the electron transport chain because the oxygen which enables the reactions to take places comes from the air. The reactions of aerobic respiration occur in the mitochondria. Some of the energy released during the reactions is stored in molecules of ATP.

How much ATP is produced during aerobic respiration?

During aerobic respiration ATP is produced from two sources:

- **substrate-level phosphorylation** – a type of chemical reaction where ATP is produced by the direct transfer of a phosphate group to ADP from another reactive substance. It occurs in the presence or absence of oxygen.

- **oxidative phosphorylation** – electrons are released during the reactions of glycolysis, the link reaction, and the Krebs cycle. The electrons are accepted by the coenzymes **nicotinamide adenine dinucleotide (NAD)** and **flavine adenine dinucleotide (FAD)** which are reduced to NADH and $FADH_2$ respectively. Ultimately the electrons are transferred from reduced NAD and FAD to oxygen which serves as the final electron acceptor. During the transfer of electrons energy is released and ATP produced. Oxidative phosphorylation occurs *only* in the presence of oxygen.

<table>
<tr><td colspan="2">Fact file</td></tr>
<tr><td colspan="2">Respiration in anaerobic conditions by</td></tr>
<tr><td>•</td><td>yeast cells produces ethanol and carbon dioxide</td></tr>
<tr><td>•</td><td>muscle cells produces lactic acid</td></tr>
<tr><td colspan="2">The processes are examples of fermentations.</td></tr>
</table>

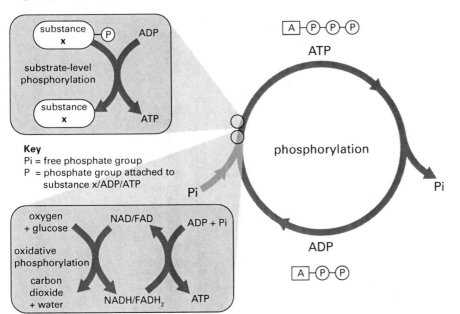

Key
Pi = free phosphate group
P = phosphate group attached to substance x/ADP/ATP

The ATP cycle

The table shows the number of molecules of ATP used and produced when a molecule of glucose is completely oxidized in the reactions of aerobic respiration.

Stage of aerobic respiration	ATP used	ATP produced by substrate-level phosphorylation	Number of reduced molecules of NAD and FAD formed	ATP produced by oxidative phosphorylation	Total production of ATP molecules
glycolysis	2	4	2NADH + H⁺	6	10
link reaction	0	0	2NADH + H⁺	6	6
Krebs cycle	0	2	6NADH + H⁺	18	24
			2FADH₂	4	
					40

Note that the net yield of ATP molecules per molecule of glucose is 38 because two molecules of ATP are used in glycolysis.

The net yield of 38 molecules of ATP following aerobic respiration represents about 40% of the potential energy contained in a molecule of glucose. The remaining 60% of energy is released as heat. In birds and mammals, the high rate of cellular respiration is the source of heat which enables them to maintain constant body temperature.

When oxygen is in short supply in cells we say that conditions are **anaerobic**. The electron transfer chain cannot work and the reactions of the Krebs cycle stop. Only the reactions of glycolysis take place. The table shows that 4 molecules of ATP are produced by substrate-level phosphorylation during glycolysis. However, 2 molecules are used so the net number of ATP molecules available following respiration in anaerobic conditions is only 2.

<table>
<tr><td>Fact file</td></tr>
<tr><td>In practice, the net yield of 38 ATP molecules produced during aerobic respiration is never reached. Losses occur because more ATP molecules are used than just those during glycolysis.</td></tr>
</table>

<table>
<tr><td colspan="2">Questions</td></tr>
<tr><td>1</td><td>Summarize the different stages of aerobic respiration.</td></tr>
<tr><td>2</td><td>Why are fewer molecules of ATP produced during anaerobic respiration than during aerobic respiration?</td></tr>
<tr><td>3</td><td>What is the difference between substrate-level phosphorylation and oxidative phosphorylation?</td></tr>
</table>

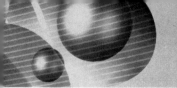

Glycolysis literally means 'splitting sugars'. A molecule of glucose – a six carbon (hexose) sugar is split into two molecules of a three carbon (triose) sugar. Each molecule of triose sugar is converted into a molecule of pyruvic acid as a pyruvate ion.

$$CH_3COCOOH \rightarrow CH_3COCOO^- + H^+$$

pyruvic acid   pyruvate ion   hydrogen ion

Glycolysis is the first stage of cellular respiration. It occurs in the cytoplasm of cells whether or not oxygen is abundant (aerobic conditions) or in short supply (anaerobic conditions).

- **Aerobic conditions** – pyruvate ions pass to Krebs cycle *via* the link reaction.
- **Anaerobic conditions** – pyruvate ions undergo a process of fermentation. Two of the most common types are lactic acid fermentation (muscle cells) and alcohol fermentation (yeast cells).

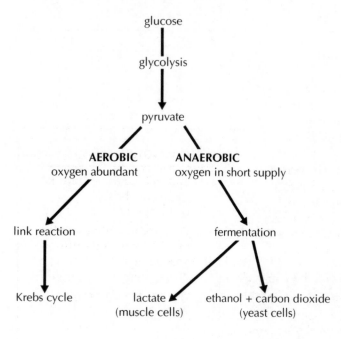

The diagrams and their checklists are your guide to the details of glycolysis and fermentation. Section **4.15** deals with the details of the link reaction and the Krebs cycle.

Fact file

Glycolysis is sometimes called the **Embden-Meyerhof pathway** after the two German biochemists who, in the 1930s, worked out its details.

Checklist: glycolysis

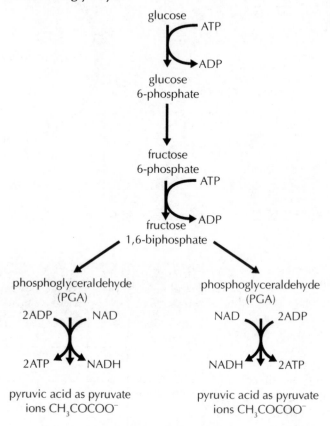

- A glucose molecule is phosphorylated. The reaction is endothermic and makes the glucose molecule more reactive. The energy comes from the hydrolysis of ATP providing a phosphate group which binds to the glucose molecule.

$$ATP \rightarrow ADP + Pi$$

Phosphorylation commits the glucose molecule to enter the sequence of reactions of glycolysis.

- Glucose-6-phosphate is converted to fructose-6-phosphate. The conversion is an isomerization.
- Further phosphorylation occurs, forming fructose 1-6 biphosphate. The reaction is endothermic and the addition of another phosphate group makes the fructose more reactive. Another molecule of ATP is used up. *Remember* that molecules of glucose and fructose each contain 6 carbon atoms.
- The molecule of fructose 1-6-biphosphate splits into two molecules of phosphorylated triose sugar, which in turn are converted in a series of reactions to pyruvate ions (you are not expected to remember the details).

The reactions are exothermic.

o Four phosphate groups are transferred from the molecules of triose sugar to ADP, forming four molecules of ATP (two molecules for each of triose sugar) by **substrate-level phosphorylation**.

o At the same time the triose sugars are oxidized. Two pairs of hydrogen atoms (one pair for each molecule of triose sugar) are released. The loss of hydrogen by each molecule of triose sugar is an example of a **dehydrogenation** reaction. Each pair of hydrogen atoms is transferred to a molecule of nicotinamide adenine dinucleotide (NAD), forming reduced NAD ($NADH + H^+$).

- The formation of pyruvate ions marks the completion of glycolysis.

Checklist: fermentation

Remember that fermentation reactions take place in anaerobic conditions (when oxygen is in short supply). In the cytoplasm, pyruvate is converted into waste products which then may be removed from the cell.

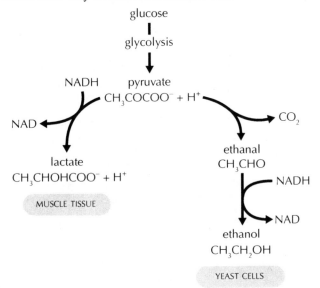

In human muscle tissue

- Pyruvate produced by glycolysis in anaerobic conditions accumulates more rapidly than can be processed via the Krebs cycle.
- Oxidation of reduced NAD (NADH) transfers hydrogen atoms to pyruvate, reducing it.
  - As a result lactate ($CH_3CHOHCOO^- + H^+$) is formed.
  - As a result pyruvate does not accumulate during glycolysis.
  - As a result NAD is regenerated and is available to accept more hydrogen atoms.
- Regeneration of NAD is required if glycolysis is to continue. Without it glycolysis would stop.
- When more oxygen becomes available lactate either
  - o undergoes reverse glycolysis synthesizing molecules of glucose, or
  - o enters the Krebs cycle where it is oxidized, forming carbon dioxide and water.
- The amount of oxygen required to metabolize excess lactate is called the **oxygen debt**.

In yeast cells

- Pyruvate produced by glycolysis in anaerobic conditions accumulates more rapidly than can be processed via the Krebs cycle.
- The carboxyl group ($-COO^-$) of pyruvate is removed as carbon dioxide. The reaction is an example of **decarboxylation** catalysed by the enzyme **decarboxylase**.
  - As a result ethanal (CH_3CHO) is formed.
- Oxidation of reduced NAD (NADH) transfers hydrogen atoms to ethanal, reducing it.
  - As a result ethanol (CH_3CH_2OH) is formed.
  - As a result pyruvate does not accumulate during glycolysis.
  - As a result NAD is regenerated and available to accept more hydrogen atoms.
- Regeneration of NAD is required if glycolysis is to continue. Without it glycolysis would stop.

Fact file

Oxygen is rarely completely absent in cells or the environment. However its concentration may be too low to oxidize all of the pyruvate produced by glycolysis. The conditions are anaerobic and different fermentation reactions oxidize the excess pyruvate, forming a variety of end products. Ethanol and lactate are common examples. Oxygen may be absent deep within rocks. We say the conditions are **hypoxic**. Some types of bacteria are found in rocks and can only live in hypoxic conditions. Oxygen poisons them.

Questions

1 At the start of glycolysis a glucose molecule is phosphorylated.
   a Explain the meaning of the statement.
   b What is the outcome of the reaction?

2 How is nicotinamide adenine dinucleotide (NAD) regenerated when
   a muscle cells
   b yeast cells
   respire anaerobically?

3 What is the oxygen debt?

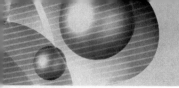
OBJECTIVES

By the end of the section you should

○ *know that pyruvate combines with coenzyme A in the link reaction to produce acetyl coenzyme A (CoA)*

○ *understand that acetyl CoA is a 2-carbon molecule which combines with a 4-carbon molecule called oxaloacetate, producing a 6-carbon molecule called citrate*

○ *know that the Krebs cycle reactions generate reduced coenzymes (NADH + H⁺ and FADH₂) and ATP by substrate level phosphorylation*

Before you start it will help to read section **4.14** (glycolysis). Also understanding key words will help you to remember the objectives of the section.

Key words

Decarboxylation – a reaction where a carboxyl group ($-COO^- + H^+$) is removed from a substance. Carbon dioxide is produced.

Dehydrogenation – a reaction where hydrogen atoms are removed from a substance.

Redox reaction – involves the passage of electrons from one substance to another. The substance losing electrons is oxidized; the substance gaining electrons is reduced (hence the name 'redox'). Energy is transferred from one side of the reaction to the other.

Remember that for each molecule of glucose entering glycolysis, two molecules of pyruvic acid (as pyruvate ions) are produced. In aerobic conditions the ions are taken up by mitochondria. Their uptake consumes ATP.

In a mitochondrion the pyruvate ions enter the link reaction, which couples glycolysis with the reactions of the Krebs cycle. The diagram and its checklist are your guide to the details of the link reaction and the Krebs cycle. Section **4.14** deals with the details of glycolysis and fermentation.

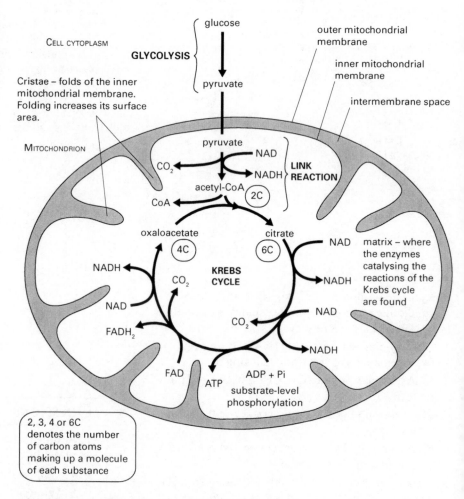

Checklist: the link reaction and the Krebs cycle

• Pyruvate passes into a mitochondrion where it is oxidized by the removal of hydrogen atoms to NAD, which is reduced to NADH. The removal of hydrogen atoms is another example of a dehydrogenation reaction catalysed by the enzyme **dehydrogenase**.

• A molecule of carbon dioxide is also released. The release is another example of a decarboxylation reaction catalysed by the enzyme **decarboxylase**.

⊚ As a result 3-carbon pyruvate is converted to a 2-carbon acetyl group.

- The acetyl group formed combines with coenzyme A (CoA), producing **acetyl coenzyme A** (abbreviated as **acetyl CoA**).

The formation of acetyl CoA couples glycolysis with the Krebs cycle: the so-called link reaction.

- The acetyl group containing 2 carbon atoms carried by CoA is transferred to the 4-carbon compound **oxaloacetic acid** (as oxaloacetate ions).

  ⊚ As a result the 6-carbon compound **citric acid** (as citrate ions) is formed.

- A cyclic sequence of reactions follows during which 2 carbon atoms, each from a different compound in the sequence, are removed in the form of carbon dioxide (CO_2). Each removal is yet another example of a decarboxylation reaction catalysed by the enzyme decarboxylase.

Also pairs of hydrogen atoms are removed, each pair from a particular compound in the sequence of reactions. Each removal is yet another example of a dehydrogenation reaction catalysed by the enzyme dehydrogenase. The hydrogen atoms either combine with NAD reducing it to NADH or FAD reducing it to $FADH_2$.

- ATP is produced by substrate-level phosphorylation.
- The formation of oxaloacetate marks the completion of the Krebs cycle. The next sequence of reactions begins with the reaction of oxaloacetate with acetyl CoA, forming citrate.

Fact file

The Krebs cycle is named after the biochemist Sir Hans Krebs who in the 1940s unravelled its sequence of reactions at Oxford University. The cycle is also known as the citric acid cycle or the **tricarboxylic acid (TCA) cycle**. Earlier in 1932, Krebs reported results of research which later helped other scientists to work out the reactions of the ornithine cycle whereby ammonia combines with carbon dioxide to form urea.

What happens next?

Hydrogen atoms removed from compounds produced by the breakdown of food molecules (e.g. glucose) during glycolysis, the link reaction and the Krebs cycle are transferred ultimately as electrons (e^-) and protons (H^+) to oxygen, forming water. The transfer of electrons is by a series of **redox** reactions along a chain of electron acceptor molecules called the **electron transport chain**. The molecules of the electron transport chain are coenzymes and proteins which are associated with the inner mitochondrial membrane.

During the transfer of electrons energy is released. The energy enables protons to be pumped from the matrix of the mitochondrion, across the inner mitochondrial membrane, into the space between the inner mitochondrial membrane and the outer mitochondrial membrane. Protons accumulate in this intermembrane space. Their return flow to the matrix is facilitated by diffusion down their concentration gradient. Energy is released. The process is called **chemiosmosis**. The energy released enables ADP and inorganic phosphate (Pi) to combine, forming ATP.

Questions

1 What is the difference between a dehydrogenation and decarboxylation reaction?

2 What is the role of acetyl CoA in aerobic respiration?

3 In which organelle of a cell and in what part of the organelle do the reactions of the Krebs cycle take place?

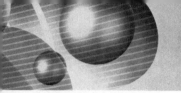

OBJECTIVES

By the end of the section you should

○ *understand that aerobic synthesis of ATP is the result of*

  ○ *transfer of electrons along an electron transport chain*

  ○ *passage of protons across the inter mitochondrial space*

○ *be able to recall the relationship between the structure of a mitochondrion and the synthesis of ATP*

Before you start it will help you to read sections **4.07** (ATP), **4.14** (glycolysis), and **4.15** (link reaction, Krebs cycle).

The synthesis of ATP by chemiosmosis is called oxidative phosphorylation because:

- the combination of ADP and Pi is a phosphorylation reaction
- oxygen is required as the final electron acceptor of the electron transport chain of proteins and coenzymes (labelled **A** to **D** and **x** and **y** respectively in the diagram below).

The diagram is your guide to the details of electron transfer and proton pumping which results in the oxidative phosphorylation of ADP forming ATP.

Transferring electrons

- During glycolysis, the link reaction, and the Krebs cycle, oxidation reactions remove hydrogen atoms from different compounds as electrons and protons.
- The reactions are coupled to the electron transport chain by the electron acceptors NAD and FAD.
- When NAD and FAD accept electrons they are reduced to NADH and $FADH_2$.
- NADH transfers electrons to protein **A** in the diagram of the electron transport chain.

○ As a result of the transfer NADH is oxidized to NAD and protein **A** is reduced.

- Electrons are transferred from reduced protein **A** to protein **C** by way of coenzyme **x**.

  ○ As a result reduced protein **A** is re-oxidized and protein **C** reduced.

- Electrons are also transferred from $FADH_2$ as part of protein **B** to protein **C** by way of coenzyme **x**.

  ○ As a result $FADH_2$ is oxidized to FAD and protein C is further reduced.

- Electrons are then transferred from reduced protein **C** to protein D by way of coenzyme **y**.

  ○ As a result reduced protein **C** is re-oxidized and protein **D** reduced.

- Electrons from reduced protein **D** are transferred with protons to oxygen. Molecules of water form and reduced protein **D** is re-oxidized, marking the end reaction of the electron transfer chain.

Pumping protons

- The redox reactions of the electron transport chain release energy which enables proteins **A, C,** and **D** to pump protons from the mitochondrial matrix across the inner mitochondrial membrane into the mitochondrial intermembrane space.

  ○ As a result protons accumulate in the intermembrane space. (*Remember* that protons carry a positive charge (H^+).)

  ○ As a result a proton gradient develops across the inner mitochondrial membrane.

- The potential difference across the inner mitochondrial membrane is –200 mV (the charge on the matrix side of the membrane is more negative than the side of the membrane facing the intermembrane space).

- The difference in charge results in an **electrochemical gradient** (of protons) and represents a store of energy.

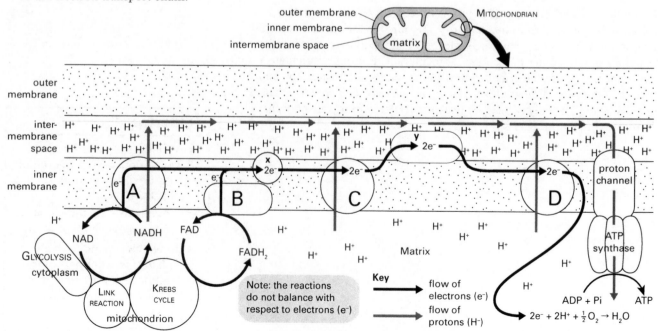

Fact file

The tendency of substances in solution to accept electrons is measured as their **redox potential**. *Remember* that when a substance accepts electrons it is reduced. The substance which donates the electrons is oxidized. Solutions with a high redox potential will tend to accept electrons from solutions with a lower redox potential.

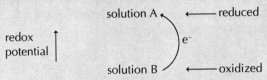

The sequence of the electron transport chains of the inner mitochondrial membrane and the thylakoid membranes of a chloroplast arises because of the difference in redox potentials between the carrier proteins. The higher its redox potential, the more likely is a carrier protein to accept electrons; the lower its redox potential the more likely is a carrier protein to donate electrons. For example $A \rightarrow D$ and **x** and **y** symbolizes the carrier proteins and coenzymes respectively associated with the inner mitochondrial membrane:

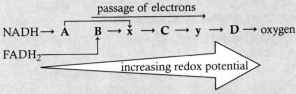

Oxygen is the final electron acceptor of the electron transport chain. Its redox potential is greater than protein **D**. The redox potential of protein **D** is greater than coenzyme **y**... and so on.

Synthesizing ATP

- Proton channels consisting of different proteins are part of the inner mitochondrial membrane.
- Each pore consists of
  - channel proteins which pass from the side of the membrane facing the intermembrane space to the matrix side of the membrane
  - the enzyme ATP synthase, which is connected by a stalk to the channel proteins and projects into the matrix of the mitochondrion
- Protons accumulated in the intermembrane space flow down the proton gradient from the space through the channel proteins and ATP synthase to the matrix (chemiosmosis).
- As a result energy is released.
- As a result ADP combines with Pi. The reaction is catalysed by ATP synthase. ATP is formed (oxidative phosphorylation).

Fact file

Recall the table on page 27 which sets out the number of ATP molecules generated when one molecule of glucose is oxidized to molecules of carbon dioxide and water during aerobic respiration. In theory, the oxidation of a molecule of NADH to NAD releases enough energy to charge the electrochemical gradient of protons (see **pumping protons**) with enough potential to generate 3 ATP molecules.

Similarly the oxidation of a molecule of $FADH_2$ to FAD releases energy with the potential of generating 2 ATP molecules. These are the values used in the table on page 27. However, it seems that NADH and $FADH_2$ generate only about 2.5 ATP and 1.5 ATP respectively, because not all of the energy stored in the proton gradient is available to generate ATP.

Qs and As

Q Cyanide is a poison. It binds with protein D of the electron transport chain shown in the diagram, preventing the transport of protons (H^+) from the mitochondrial matrix into the intermembrane space. Explain why a person who ingests (takes in) cyanide might die.

A *Your answer should include some (and preferably all) of the following points:*

- *a proton gradient does not develop*
- *protons do not flow through the channel proteins and ATP synthase*
- *ATP is not formed by oxidative phosphorylation*
- *the Krebs cycle and the link reaction stop*
- *ATP is only formed by substrate-level phosphorylation during glycolysis*
- *lactate builds up*

Fact file

Thermogenesis refers to heat production as the result of chemiosmosis which is uncoupled from the synthesis of ATP. Uncoupling occurs because of a protein called **thermogenin** as part of the inner mitochondrial membrane found in the mitochondria of some types of cell, e.g. brown fat cells. The protein provides an alternative pathway for the flow of electrons from the mitochondrial intermembrane space to the matrix. The energy released results in the dispersal of heat in thermogenesis rather than ATP synthesis. The heat helps to warm animals hibernating during cold weather, and babies which are vulnerable to heat loss because of their small size.

Questions

1. Why does their small size make babies vulnerable to the rapid loss of body heat?
2. What is the meaning of the term redox potential?
3. Summarize the process and the outcome of chemiosmosis.

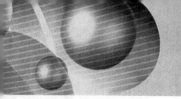
OBJECTIVES

By the end of the section you should

○ *know that photosynthesis is the main route by which energy enters an ecosystem*

○ *understand that energy is transferred through trophic levels and is dissipated*

○ *be able to describe and explain pyramids of numbers, biomass and energy, and their relationship to food chains and webs*

Before you start it will help to read sections **4.01** (community, niche) and **4.08** (photosynthesis).

The community works through the interactions between its different niches. *Remember* that **food** is an important part of the niche idea.

Ⓡ As a result describing feeding relationships is one way of finding out how a community works.

Food chains and food webs

Different words are used to describe the feeding relationships between the plants and animals of a community.

- **Producers** make food (sugars). Plants are producers. So too are some types of single celled organisms and algae. They make food by **photosynthesis**. Food chains and food webs always begin with producers.
- **Consumers** take in food (feeding) already formed. Animals are consumers.

A **food chain** shows the links between producers and consumers. It describes one pathway of food through a community. For example:

oak leaves ⟶ slugs ⟶ thrush ⟶ sparrowhawk

A **food web** describes all possible feeding relationships of a community. It consists of interlinked food chains. The diagram shows the food web in an oakwood.

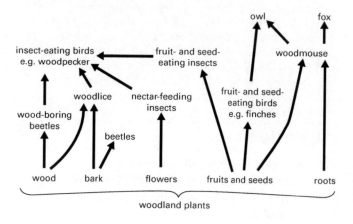

Ecological pyramids

Food webs represent the feeding relationships of communities but do not indicate the numbers of individuals involved. The description is **qualitative**. Ecological pyramids represent a **quantitative** description of feeding relationships. They describe *how much* food is transferred through the community.

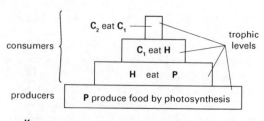

Key
P = plants   H = herbivores C_1 = first carnivores
C_2 = second carnivores

Notice that organisms with *similar* types of food are grouped into **trophic** (feeding) **levels**.

- The producer trophic level occupies the base of the pyramid.
- Other trophic levels are made up of consumers:
  ○ **primary** consumers are herbivores (H)
  ○ **secondary** consumers or first/primary carnivores (C_1) feed on herbivores
  ○ **tertiary** consumers or second/secondary carnivores (C_2) feed on first/primary carnivores

There are different types of ecological pyramid.

- **Pyramids of numbers** represent the number of organisms in each trophic level at a particular time. The diagram compares the pyramid of numbers for a grassland community and a woodland community.

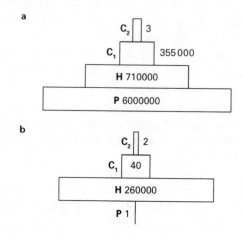

Pyramids of numbers for **a** grassland and **b** woodland communities.

Notice that for the grassland community

- a lot of producers (grass plants) support many herbivores (e.g. insects), which in turn support fewer carnivores (e.g. spiders).

  Ⓡ As a result the pyramid is upright and tapers to a point.

Notice that for the woodland community
- few producers (trees) support many herbivores (e.g. insect larvae), which in turn support fewer carnivores (e.g. birds, spiders).
  - ☯ As a result the pyramid points down as well as up.

What is the problem?

The producers and consumers in the grassland community are mostly small, so differences in size are slight and do not have a marked effect on the shape of the pyramid. However the pyramid of numbers for the woodland community does not take into account the big differences in size of the producers and consumers. Each tree is large and can meet the food needs of many smaller consumers.

- **Pyramids of biomass** represent the amount of organic material in each trophic level (**standing crop** or **standing crop biomass**) at a *particular time*.

The diagram shows the pyramid of biomass for a woodland.

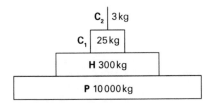

Notice that the pyramid is upright and tapers to a point. Measuring the standing crop in each trophic level allows for differences in size of producers and consumers.

But there are still problems!

- The biomass of an organism can vary during the year. For example, a tree in full leaf during the summer has a much greater biomass than in winter without its leaves.
- The diagram shows a pyramid of biomass for the English Channel. *Notice* that the pyramid points down.

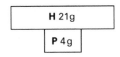

- o The producers do not live as long as the herbivores which depend on them but reproduce quickly.
- o The rapid turnover of producers means that, for a time, the standing crop of producers may be smaller than the herbivores.
- o No account is taken of the *rate* at which biomass is produced or consumed. Only the amount of organic material in each trophic level at a *particular time* (standing crop – see above) counts in a pyramid of biomass.

- **Pyramids of energy** take account of the amount of organic material produced and consumed over a *period of time*. The organic matter represents a store of energy. The diagram shows a pyramid of energy for a stream. It illustrates the energy flow through, and energy loss, from the trophic levels of the community.

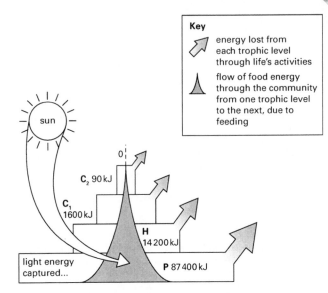

Key

energy lost from each trophic level through life's activities

flow of food energy through the community from one trophic level to the next, due to feeding

Pyramid of energy for a stream in kJ m^{-2} year^{-1}

Notice:

- The energy that flows through trophic levels of the community begins with sunlight, which enables producers to produce food by photosynthesis.
- The food produced flows through the community because the consumers of a particular trophic level feed on the producers/consumers of the preceding trophic level.
  - ☯ As a result food energy is transferred from one trophic level to the next.
- At each trophic level some of the food energy is used by organisms to fuel their own metabolism. The energy is eventually lost as heat from the community.
  - ☯ As a result the transfer of energy between trophic levels is never 100% efficient.
  - ☯ As a result the amount of energy decreases as it flows from one trophic level to the next through the community.
  - ☯ As a result the pyramid of energy tapers to a point.

But there are still problems with ecological pyramids!

- Many organisms feed at several trophic levels.
- Not all parts of a plant produce food or are available to herbivores. Roots are buried and do not contain chlorophyll. Yet the whole plant contributes to the data for the producer trophic level.
- The flow of food energy through decomposers is often omitted from pyramid diagrams.

Questions

1 What is a trophic level?

2 List the different types of consumer and briefly explain what each type eats.

3 Why is the pyramid of biomass usually a better description of feeding relationships in a community than a pyramid of numbers?

OBJECTIVES

OBJECTIVES

By the end of the section you should be able to

○ *describe the flow of energy through food chains and food webs*

○ *explain how energy is dissipated from food chains to the environment*

○ *discuss the efficiency of energy transfer between trophic levels*

Before you start it will help to read sections **4.01** (decomposers), **4.08** (photosynthesis), **4.17** (food chains, pyramids of energy), and **4.20** (decomposers).

Light energy is trapped and converted by producers into the chemical bond energy of sugars by the reactions of photosynthesis. Energy flows through food chains and food webs when

- **herbivores** feed on plants
- **carnivores** feed on herbivores and other carnivores
- **decomposers** feed on dead organic material

In other words, feeding transfers energy between trophic levels: producers → consumers

Energy flow

Sunlight underpins the existence of most of life on Earth. Without sunlight and the producers which convert its energy into food energy by photosynthesis, most communities would not exist. The diagram tracks the flow of energy between trophic levels: producer → herbivore → carnivore. Follow the sequence of the checklist ❶ – ❺ which refer to the diagram. Together, the diagram and checklist will help you to quantify the efficiency of energy transfer between trophic levels.

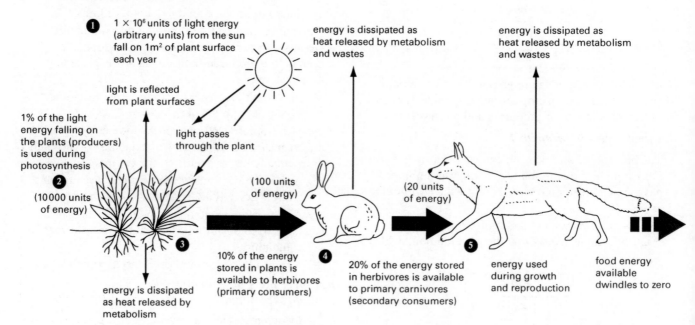

Checklist

❶ • Most of the sunlight reaching the Earth's upper atmosphere
  ○ is reflected by clouds, dust particles, and the Earth's surface
  ○ heats the atmosphere and the Earth's surface
  ○ causes the evaporation of water

❷ • **Productivity** is the rate at which biomass is produced by an ecosystem. It is determined by the rate at which producers make food by photosynthesis.
  • **Gross primary production (GPP)** refers to the biomass of food produced in $g\ m^{-2}$ (of plant surface exposed to sunlight) $year^{-1}$.
  • **Net primary production (NPP)** refers to GPP less the biomass used by consumers to fuel their own metabolism. NPP is used to compare the productivity of different ecosystems.

Fact file

Fragments of dead material (e.g. twigs, leaves) form **detritus**. Animals which feed on detritus are called detritivores.

Ecosystem	NPP g m^{-2} yr^{-1}
coral reefs	2600
tropical rain forests	2150
temperate deciduous forests	1300
temperate grasslands	500
open ocean	130
hot desert	65

3 • Some parts of plants may not be palatable (e.g. bitter tasting leaves) or accessible (e.g. roots) to herbivores.

    As a result the parts are not eaten and therefore not part of the food energy available to herbivores.

4 • Animals do not produce enzymes that digest cellulose and lignin.

    As a result plant material is difficult to digest.

• Herbivores depend on microorganisms living in the gut to produce enzymes which digest cellulose and lignin. The process is inefficient.

    As a result herbivores produce a large amount of faeces which contains undigested plant material, representing energy not available to carnivores.

5 • Animal material is easier to digest than plant material.

• Animal material has a higher energy value than plant material.

    As a result the transfer of energy from herbivore → carnivore is more efficient (20%) than producer → herbivore (5–10%).

• The indigestible parts of prey (hooves, hides, bones) represent energy not available to other carnivores.

Notice that energy is dissipated (dispersed) from the food chain to the environment at each stage of energy transfer between the sun and trophic levels: sun → producer; producer → primary consumer (herbivore); primary consumer (herbivore) → secondary consumer (primary carnivore)... and so on.

In summary:

• Assume that 1×10^6 units of solar light energy (arbitrary units) are available to the trophic levels of the food chain. *Notice* that only 20 units of chemical energy (as food) are available to primary carnivores.

    As a result the number of trophic levels is limited: usually 3 to 4.

• The more productive the ecosystem (the greater is the producer biomass), the more trophic levels there are: usually a maximum of 6.

Energy flow through decomposers

The flow of energy through decomposers and detritivores is often left out of diagrams representing food chains, food webs, and ecological pyramids. *Remember*, however, that in some communities, 80% of the productivity of a trophic level may flow through decomposer food chains.

• The energy locked up in the remains of dead organisms and wastes (faeces and urine) enters decomposer food chains where the activities of fungi and bacteria break down the organic material.

   ○ In tropical rain forests, the warm moist environment promotes the activities of decomposers.

    As a result the rate of decomposition is rapid.

    As a result little organic material accumulates in the ecosystem.

    As a result the soil of rain forests is nutrient poor.

   ○ In peat bogs the cold, wet, acidic environment inhibits the activities of decomposers.

    As a result the rate of decomposition is slow.

    As a result much organic material accumulates, forming **peat**.

Qs and As

Q Why are there a limited number of trophic levels in an ecological pyramid and links in a food chain?

A *The number of trophic levels and links in a food chain is limited by the food energy available. As the amount of food energy passing from one trophic level to the next decreases, so does the amount of living material that can be supported in each trophic level. When food energy dwindles to zero, trophic levels and links in food chains can no longer exist.*

Q Why is a pyramid of energy the best way of representing feeding relationships between organisms in different trophic levels?

A *Pyramids of numbers and biomass represent feeding relationships at a particular time. A pyramid of energy represents feeding relationships over a period of time. In other words, it takes account of the rate of production and consumption of biomass and deals with problems of*

• *differences in the size of organisms*

• *seasonal variations of biomass*

• *the rapid turnover of small organisms relative to the consumers that depend on them*

Questions

1 How does the description of the flow of energy through the community help us understand why there is a limited number of links in a food chain?

2 Suggest why the productivity of tropical rain forests is greater than temperate grasslands.

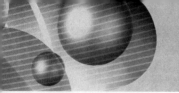

OBJECTIVES

By the end of the section you should

○ *be able to compare the energy input and productivity of natural ecosystems with those based on intensive farming*

○ *understand the ways in which productivity is affected by farming practices*

Before you start it will help to read section **4.08** (photosynthesis) and **4.18** (energy transfer).

Farms are ecosystems with people as consumers in a food chain of crops and livestock. The amount of food produced depends on

• energy *input*: sunlight and fuel oil

• energy *output*: efficiency of the conversion of energy input into the energy content of the food produced (crops and livestock)

The different practices which help to maximize the amount of food produced are what is called **intensive farming**.

Energy inputs and outputs have values. The diagram shows the energy values of different inputs and outputs for a modern intensive farm of 460 hectares in Southern England.

Photosynthetic efficiency is a measure of how well the plants of an ecosystem convert light energy into the chemical energy stored in the bonds of sugar molecules by photosynthesis.

$$\frac{\text{photosynthetic}}{\text{efficiency}} = \frac{\text{energy content of plants year}^{-1}}{\text{light energy available year}^{-1}}$$

The greater the photosynthetic efficiency, the greater is the productivity (measured as net primary productivity) of the ecosystem.

• In natural ecosystems photosynthetic efficiency (and therefore productivity) varies depending on temperature, rainfall, and concentration of carbon dioxide.

   ◉ As a result values for photosynthetic efficiency vary between 0.5% and 1% of the total energy value of sunlight reaching ground level.

• The photosynthetic efficiency of farm crops grown intensively may range up to 6%.

If we assume that the energy input of sunlight into farm ecosystems is the same as natural ecosystems…

then… the difference in photosynthetic efficiency (and productivity) between farm crops and the plants of natural ecosystems is due to the non-sun energy inputs into intensive farms. The inputs are based on fuel oil. More than 40% is used directly as fuel; the rest indirectly because the manufacture of farm machinery, pesticides, fertilizers, animal feeds, etc. depends on oil.

Farming practices

Different farming practices aim to increase productivity by:

• maximizing the rate of photosynthesis and therefore the growth of crops

• reducing losses in productivity because of
   ○ weeds which compete with crops for space and nutrients
   ○ animals (mainly insects) which eat crops and spread plant disease
   ○ fungi which cause plant diseases
   ○ the dissipation of energy raising livestock

Pesticides

Pests are organisms that reduce productivity by destroying crops and harming livestock. Pesticides are substances that kill pests and therefore help to increase productivity.

• *Insecticides* kill insects.

• *Herbicides* kill weeds.

• *Fungicides* kill fungi.

Pesticides are applied to crops as sprays, fogs, or granules and to livestock as dusts or dips.

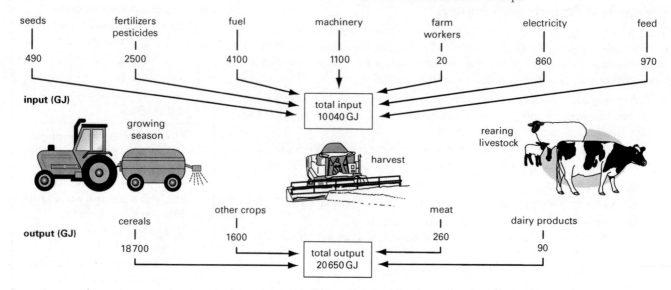

Energy inputs and outputs on a modern intensive farm; 1 GJ (gigajoules) = 10^3 MJ (megajoules) = 10^9 J (joules)

Fertilizers

The growth (and therefore productivity) of crops depends on elements and compounds (**nutrients**) that occur naturally in soil. Substances which add nutrients to soil are called **fertilizers**. They help to increase productivity by replacing the nutrients that crops take from the soil during the growing season. The table lists the ions of some of the elements that crops need in relatively large amounts.

The ions of other elements are needed by plants in much smaller amounts (measured in tens of ppm or less). Many of them act as enzyme co-factors.

Nutrient	ppm*	Ion	% of crop dry mass	Requirement
nitrogen	15 000	NO_3^-	3.5	synthesis of amino acids, proteins, and nucleic acids
potassium	10 000	K^+	3.4	enzyme co-factor, opening of stomata
calcium	5000	Ca^{2+}	0.7	formation of the plant cell wall
phosphorus	2000	PO_4^{3-}	0.4	synthesis of ATP and nucleic acids
magnesium	2000	Mg^{2+}	0.1	synthesis of chlorophyll
sulfur	1000	SO_4^{2-}	0.1	synthesis of some amino acids

*ppm = parts per million in solution

- **Natural fertilizers** (organic material such as manure and compost) are spread on soil. They help to maintain its structure. Fungi and bacteria decompose the material releasing nutrients which are absorbed by crops.
- **Artificial fertilizers** are added to soil as sprays or granules. Most supply nitrogen (N), phosphorus (P) and potassium (K) – the so called **NPK** fertilizers.

Rearing livestock

Livestock raised intensively are usually kept indoors. The aim is to reduce the dissipation of energy as heat from the animals so that they grow more quickly. The heat is released during cellular respiration.

- Confinement of animals in pens or cages restricts their movement.
  - Ⓔ As a result cellular respiration during muscle contraction is reduced.
  - Ⓔ As a result the energy dissipated in exercise is reduced.
- Their environment (heating, lighting) is controlled.
  - Ⓔ As a result the temperature difference between the environment and animals bodies is reduced.
  - Ⓔ As a result the energy dissipated in their keeping warm is reduced.

Rearing livestock intensively is sometimes called **factory farming**. The animals gain weight more quickly than those allowed to roam outdoors free range. Productivity therefore increases.

Costs and welfare

The ethical issues arising from modern intensive farming include

- costs to the environment
- the welfare of livestock

Fact file

In simple terms, estimates suggest that the practices of modern intensive farming increase productivity at a non-sun energy cost each year equivalent to more than 11 tonnes of oil for every person involved in the industry. The costs to the environment arise from the practices which increase productivity and which are the result of oil inputs.

- the use of pesticides which are poisonous and kill wildlife as well as pests – they may be a hazard to human health.
- the use of fertilizers which drain from land into water causing **eutrophication** – they may also be a hazard to human health.
- the use of modern farm machinery which works most efficiently in large open fields.
  - Ⓔ As a result the farming landscape is cleared of hedgerows, copses and woods.
  - Ⓔ As a result the biodiversity of ecosystems is reduced and genetic diversity lost.

Is it fair for livestock to be reared intensively so that we can enjoy eating more meat? Confining animals indoors causes them physical discomfort, boredom, and frustration. Some people argue this is cruel. Others claim that animals raised indoors must be content because they are safe from predators, sheltered, and eat well. However, we know that overeating in humans is a common sign of depression.

Questions

1 Use the data to calculate the energy value of the sun's input for a farm of 640 hectares.

   Energy received at ground level = 0.35 MJ cm^{-2} yr^{-1} (100 million cm^2 = 1 hectare).

2 Using the answer from question 1 with the following data, calculate the amount of light energy converted into crop biomass each year.
   - Photosynthetic efficiency = 0.8%
   - Average crop cover = 50%
   - Length of time crops cover the soil each year = 6 months

3 For every 1 m^{-2} of grass it eats, a cow obtains 3000 kJ of energy. It uses 100 kJ in growth, 1000 kJ are lost as body heat, and 1900 kJ are lost in faeces.

   a What percentage of the energy in 1 m^2 of grass
      (i) is used in growth, and
      (ii) passes through gut as food which is not absorbed?

   b If beef has an energy value of 12 kJ g^{-1}, how many m^2 of grass are needed to produce 100 g of beef?

4.20 Nutrient cycles

OBJECTIVES

By the end of the section you should

O *know that chemical elements are recycled in ecosystems*

O *understand that microorganisms play a key role in recycling elements*

Before you start it will help you to read sections **4.01** (decomposers), **4.08** (photosynthesis), and **4.13** (respiration).

Fact file

Six of the most common elements found in the environment make up more than 95% of living matter. They are:

• carbon (C)   • hydrogen (H)
• nitrogen (N)   • oxygen (O)
• phosphorus (P) • sulfur (S)

If the letter symbols of the elements are arranged in order, they can be easily remembered as **CHNOPS**.

The chemical compounds formed from the elements taken from the environment by organisms are nutrients essential for healthy life. When organisms die, nutrients are released into the environment by the

• *physical processes* of climate
• *biochemical processes* of respiration and photosynthesis
• *saprobiontic activities* of bacteria and fungi

Fungi and bacteria are called saprobionts because they feed on dead organic matter. Their feeding activities cause decomposition which is why they are also called **decomposers**.

The processes of decomposition release mineral nutrients and gases into the environment.

The carbon cycle

The concept map and its checklist are your revision guide to the carbon cycle.

Checklist: the carbon cycle

1 • The atmosphere is a source of carbon as the gas carbon dioxide.
• Carbon dioxide in solution is a source of carbon in water.

2 • The oxidation of sugar during respiration releases carbon dioxide into the environment.
• Carbon dioxide released into the environment *enters* the atmosphere or passes into solution.

3 • During photosynthesis the carbon of carbon dioxide is fixed (becomes part of) sugars produced by photoautotrophs.
  As a result carbon is *removed* from the environment.

4 • Deposition of carbonates (as chalk limestone) forms **sediments** which are a reservoir of carbon because carbon dioxide in solution is absorbed by
  o plant-like single-celled organisms called phytoplankton and used in photosynthesis
  o animals such as aquatic snails which make their shells from carbonates
  As a result carbon is *removed* from the environment

5 • Combustion of fossil fuels (coal, oil, gas, peat) releases carbon dioxide into the atmosphere.
  As a result carbon *enters* the environment.

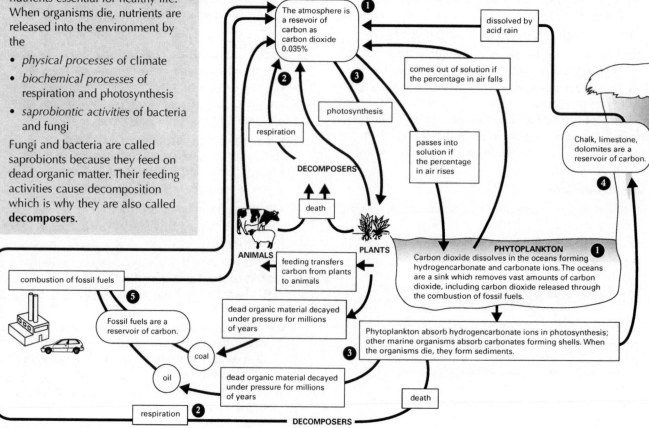

The nitrogen cycle

The concept map and its checklist are your revision guide to the nitrogen cycle.

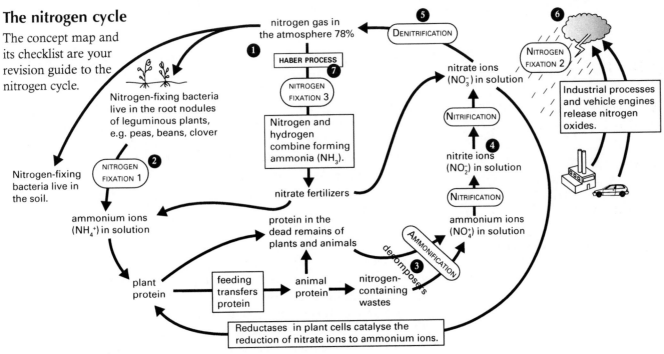

Checklist: the nitrogen cycle

❶ • Nitrogen is the most abundant gas in the atmosphere.
  • Most organisms *cannot* use gaseous nitrogen directly.

❷ • Some types of bacteria called **nitrogen fixing** bacteria have **nitrogenase** enzymes which catalyse the combination of gaseous nitrogen with hydrogen, forming ammonia (NH_3). In solution ammonia forms ammonium ions (NH_4^+).
  • Plants take up ammonium ions in solution through their roots (plants also take up nitrate ions in solution) enabling them to synthesize nucleic acids and proteins.
  • Feeding transfers nitrogen (as nitrogen containing compounds) from producers → consumers through food chains.

❸ • **Ammonification** refers to the enzyme-catalysed reactions which break down dead organisms and nitrogen containing wastes. A variety of decomposers are responsible.
  ⊛ As a result ammonium ions (NH_4^+) are formed.

❹ • **Nitrification** refers to the oxidation reactions carried out by **nitrifying bacteria**. The reactions convert ammonium (NH_4^+) compounds to nitrites (NO_2^-) and then to nitrates (NO_3^-).
  ⊛ As a result nitrogen as nitrates (NO_3^-) is available in a form that is most easily absorbed by the roots of plants.

❺ • **Dentrification** refers to the reduction reactions carried out by **dentrifying bacteria**. The reactions convert nitrate ions (NO_3^-) to nitrogen gas (N_2).
  ⊛ As a result nitrogen gas enters the atmosphere.

❻ • Lightning is a high energy discharge which breaks apart nitrogen molecules. The nitrogen atoms produced react with atmospheric oxygen.
  ⊛ As a result nitrogen oxides form, which dissolve in rain drops. Nitric acid (HNO_3) and nitrous acid (HNO_2) are produced.
  • The acids react with compounds in the soil, forming nitrates (NO_3^-) and nitrites (NO_2^-).

❼ • The Haber reaction is an industrial process which fixes nitrogen in combination with hydrogen producing ammonia (NH_3).
  • Some of the ammonia is used to make nitrate fertilizers.
  ⊛ As a result crop production is improved.

Fact file

Nitrate ions absorbed by plant cells are reduced nitrate ions and then ammonium ions before becoming part of nucleic acids, proteins, and other nitrogen containing compounds. The reduction reactions are catalysed by **reductase** enzymes.

Fact file

The conversion of ammonium compounds into nitrates (nitrification) releases energy which is then available to drive the metabolism of the bacteria responsible. The reactions are an example of **chemosynthesis**. The bacteria are referred to as **chemoautotrophs**.

Questions

1 Outline the stages in the carbon cycle and nitrogen cycle and compare them.

2 Why are fields sown with leguminous crops (e.g. peas and beans) in 'rotation' with other crops?

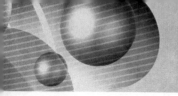
OBJECTIVES

By the end of the section you should

○ *know what leaching is*

○ *understand the process of eutrophication*

○ *understand the significance of the enhanced greenhouse effect leading to global warming*

Before you start it will help to read sections **4.03** (distribution of organisms), **4.12** (greenhouses), **4.19** (fertilizers), and **4.20** (carbon cycle, nitrogen cycle).

Agrochemicals (pesticides and fertilizers) **leach** (remove in solution) from the soil into rivers, lakes, and the sea. People produce sewage which (treated and untreated) passes into rivers and the sea.

Fertilizers and sewage are organic wastes which are a source of nutrients for bacteria and other microorganisms living in water. As the water becomes richer and richer in nutrients the microorganisms multiply and rapidly increase in numbers. This process is called **eutrophication**.

• Aerobic bacteria decompose organic wastes.

　🌐 As a result, poisonous substances (e.g. ammonia) are released into solution.

• Oxygen in solution is used up.

　🌐 As a result fish and other wildlife living in the water die because of poisoning and/or lack of oxygen.

• Anaerobic bacteria continue the breakdown of the organic wastes.

　🌐 As a result the water supports only those organisms able to survive when the concentration of oxygen in solution is low.

　🌐 As a result biodiversity is reduced.

The flow chart on the left summarizes the sequence of events.

Indicator species

The diagram shows what happens to the biodiversity of a river polluted with sewage.

• The more sewage there is in the water, the less oxygen there is in solution.

　🌐 As a result, there are fewer species able to survive in the polluted parts of the river.

The presence or absence of different species indicates how polluted the water is with sewage. The species in question are called **indicator species**.

Sewage enters the water.

↓

The number of microorganisms increases rapidly.

↓

aerobic conditions

The activities of the microorganisms breaking down the sewage use up dissolved oxygen

most types of organism die because of the lack of oxygen

anaerobic conditions

a few types of organism can survive the lack of oxygen

↓

their numbers increase

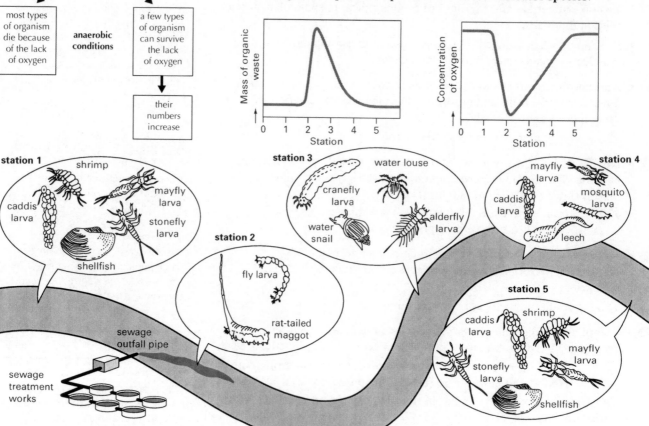

The presence or absence of different species of animal indicates how polluted the water is with sewage. *Note* that the number of species and types of species at Stations 2, 3, and 4 are less than at Stations 1 and 5. The species found at Station 5 are the same as those found in unpolluted waters at Station 1. The dilution of sewage means that water quality is no longer affected.

The greenhouse effect

The Sun radiates large amounts of heat into space. *Remember* the term **radiation** refers to the transfer of heat from one object to another, even though the objects are not touching. Earth is much cooler than the Sun. Its surface, therefore, absorbs the Sun's radiant heat and warms up. As a result, the surface gives out radiant heat which is absorbed by water vapour, carbon dioxide, and other gases in the atmosphere. The diagram shows what happens.

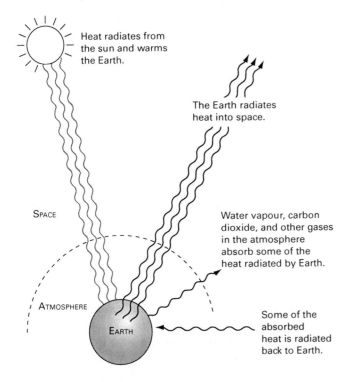

Heat radiates from the sun and warms the Earth.

The Earth radiates heat into space.

SPACE

Water vapour, carbon dioxide, and other gases in the atmosphere absorb some of the heat radiated by Earth.

ATMOSPHERE

EARTH

Some of the absorbed heat is radiated back to Earth.

The gases radiate the heat back to Earth's surface, keeping Earth warmer than it would otherwise be. The warming effect is called the **greenhouse effect**. We are alive because of the greenhouse effect. Without it, Earth's surface would be very cold.

Fact file

Inside a greenhouse

The Sun's radiant heat passes easily through the glass of a greenhouse. The plants in the greenhouse are at a much lower temperature. They absorb the Sun's energy, warm up, and radiate heat. The heat cannot escape through the glass. Instead the glass **re-radiates** it back into the greenhouse, which therefore warms up. Because water vapour, carbon dioxide, and other gases in the atmosphere act like the glass in a greenhouse, they are called **greenhouse gases**.

Global warming

Earth's surface has warmed up by 0.75°C during the last century. The rate of warming is increasing. The term **global warming** refers to this increase.

Why is global warming taking place?

Many scientists think that we are responsible for global warming. Worldwide our activities release more and more greenhouse gases into the air, adding to the natural greenhouse effect of the atmosphere.

Carbon dioxide is a natural greenhouse gas.

- Each year we send more than 6000 million tonnes of carbon as carbon dioxide into the air due to burning fossil fuels in power stations, factories, and motor vehicles.
- We are felling too many trees. For example, clearing rain forest (deforestation) means that there are fewer trees to take carbon dioxide from the air by photosynthesis.
- Burning felled trees releases even more carbon dioxide into the air.

Methane is another natural greenhouse gas.

- Methane is produced by the millions of bacteria that live in the anaerobic environment of a cow's stomach. The bacteria help to digest the cow's food. The cow releases the methane through its anus to the air.
- Rice is grown in fields covered with water. Bacteria in the soil produce methane because there is very little oxygen in solution in the waterlogged soil.
- As more cows are raised for meat and milk, and more rice is grown, so more methane is produced and released into the air.
- Some greenhouse gases are produced only as a result of human activities. **Nitrogen oxides** and **chlorofluorohydrocarbons (CFCs)** are examples.
- Nitrogen oxides are formed from burning fossil fuels in power stations and engines.
- CFCs come from the propellants in aerosols, foam, and the liquids that cool freezers.

What will happen?

Global warming will upset normal weather patterns.

- The amount of cloud cover, the force and direction of winds, and rainfall patterns will all change.
  - As a result, areas of the world with high rainfall will experience even more rain.
  - As a result, areas with low rainfall will become even drier and perhaps turn to desert.
  - As a result the distribution and numbers of wild animals and plants will change.
  - Some species many become extinct
  - Other species may increase in numbers. An increase in insect pests, for example, would damage crops and livestock, reducing food supplies.

Global warming is causing the polar ice caps to melt.

- Melt water flowing into the oceans is causing sea levels to rise. Over the 21st century levels could rise by as much as 1.5 metres.
  - As a result there would be widespread flooding and low-lying areas of land would disappear under the sea.

Questions

1 Outline the process of eutrophication.

2 What is an indicator species?

3 Summarize the possible consequences of global warming.

4.22   Succession

OBJECTIVES

By the end of the section you should

○ *know that a community is not static but a dynamic unit which changes over time*

○ *understand that a community passes through a series of successional changes each called a sere*

○ *know that during a succession biodiversity increases*

○ *know the difference between a primary succession and secondary succession*

○ *understand that conservation of environment often depends on human management of succession*

Before you start it will help to read sections **4.01** (community) and **4.18** (flow of energy).

Fact file

The flow of energy through a climax community is at a maximum.

Communities do not stay the same forever. They change over time as one community gives way to another. The process is called **succession**. The communities of a succession are each called a **sere**. A sere can be recognized by the collection of species that dominate at that point in a succession.

A succession begins with the colonization of a new environment which is clear of organisms because of a **disturbance**. The colonizers are called **pioneers** and form a **pioneer community** of producers and consumers. The final sere of a succession is called the **climax community**, which is stable. Its species make up does not change over time unless a disturbance removes them. The idea is the same for any succession. Here the diagram shows the succession of a pond as an example.

Notice:

- The different species of the pond community forming a sere impact on their own environment, altering it. The changes may favour the colonization of new species rather than the survival of the original species causing the changes.
  - Ⓔ As a result the previously dominant species may die out to be replaced by the new species.
- As the succession develops, the community of each sere is more **biodiverse** (made up of more species) than the community of the previous sere.
  - Ⓔ As a result the flow of energy through the community increases from one sere to the next.
  - Ⓔ As a result the productivity of the ecosystem increases as the succession develops.
  - Ⓔ As a result the biomass of the community of a sere is greater than the biomass of the community of the sere preceding it.
- Succession is directional. The different serial stages in a particular succession (e.g. pond) can be predicted.

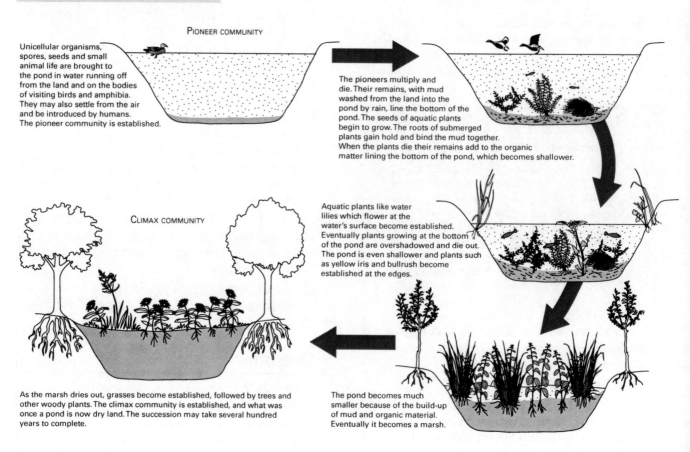

PIONEER COMMUNITY

Unicellular organisms, spores, seeds and small animal life are brought to the pond in water running off from the land and on the bodies of visiting birds and amphibia. They may also settle from the air and be introduced by humans. The pioneer community is established.

The pioneers multiply and die. Their remains, with mud washed from the land into the pond by rain, line the bottom of the pond. The seeds of aquatic plants begin to grow. The roots of submerged plants gain hold and bind the mud together. When the plants die their remains add to the organic matter lining the bottom of the pond, which becomes shallower.

Aquatic plants like water lilies which flower at the water's surface become established. Eventually plants growing at the bottom of the pond are overshadowed and die out. The pond is even shallower and plants such as yellow iris and bullrush become established at the edges.

The pond becomes much smaller because of the build-up of mud and organic material. Eventually it becomes a marsh.

CLIMAX COMMUNITY

As the marsh dries out, grasses become established, followed by trees and other woody plants. The climax community is established, and what was once a pond is now dry land. The succession may take several hundred years to complete.

The serial stages in the succession of a pond

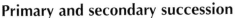

Primary and secondary succession

Succession which begins when organisms colonize an environment where previously living things were absent is called **primary succession**.

- Islands formed from volcanic eruptions (the disturbance) undersea are examples of environments where the organisms of a pioneer community establish a primary succession on the bare rock.
- Lichens are one of the few types of organism able to survive in such hostile conditions. Their activities break down the rock into particles. Their dead remains decompose, adding nutrients to the mixture, forming soil in which the species of the next sere can establish a foothold.

Succession which begins when organisms colonize an environment where previously living things were established is called a **secondary succession**.

- Land cleared for agriculture or forest destroyed by fire (the disturbances) are examples of environments bare of wildlife. However, recolonization quickly takes places if circumstances allow. Surviving seeds, spores, and the parts of plants buried underground and capable of asexual reproduction are the starting point for a new succession. In time the climax community is re-established if the succession is undisturbed.
- Succession occurs on different time scales, ranging from a few days to hundreds of years. For example, the development of a climax woodland may take hundreds of years; the succession of insects and fungi in a pat of cow dung may take just a few months.

How science works (F)

Some communities seem to be stable and remain unchanged for long periods of time. Their stability, however, is the result of human activities. For example, we think of moorland as 'natural'. However, the moorland environment is the result of clearance of the climax community of woodland to allow grazing (the disturbance) by livestock.

In other words moorland is sub-climatic, but persists because long-term **grazing** deflects the succession from its climax. Grazing destroys seedling trees, so that the climax community of woodland cannot develop. We call moorland a **plagioclimax**.

Moorland has amenity value (we enjoy the landscape for its beauty and leisure opportunities). Our understanding of how to manage its succession through grazing by livestock long-term underpins the **conservation** of a highly prized environment.

A mowed lawn is another example of deflected succession resulting in a plagioclimax – providing that mowing (the disturbance) occurs regularly. However, if the lawn is left uncut daisies and dandelions soon appear, followed by a range of other flowering plants as succession gets underway. If the lawn is left for a few years, woody plants grow up and overshadow the grass, which dies out.

Fact file

Conservation

Our well-being depends on keeping a balance between using resources and protecting the environments from where the resources come. Conservation enables us to

- use renewable resources (plants, animals) in a sustainable way
- reduce our use of non-renewable resources (metals, fossil fuels) through recycling and the discovery of alternative materials for the production of goods
- use land so that conflicting interests between human needs and the impact of these needs on the survival of plants and animals and their environments are reduced
- reduce pollution by the development of more efficient industrial processes, which produce less waste and use less energy
- introduce more environmentally friendly methods of farming

Different schemes help to protect wildlife in danger of extinction (**endangered species**) as a result of our activities.

Questions

1. What is the difference between a primary succession and a secondary succession?
2. Briefly describe the relationship between flow of energy through and productivity of the communities of a succession from pioneer to climax.
3. What is a plagioclimax?

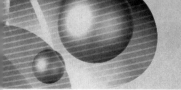
OBJECTIVES

By the end of the section you should

○ *know the meanings of key words*

○ *be able to use genetic diagrams to predict the results of different monohybrid crosses*

○ *be able to use genetic diagrams to predict crosses involving multiple alleles and sex linked characteristics*

Key words

Alleles – a pair of genes at the same position (locus) on homologous chromosomes

Homozygote – the alleles at a specific locus controlling a particular characteristic are identical

Heterozygote – the alleles at a specific locus controlling a particular characteristic are different

Dominant – any characteristic controlled by an allele that appears in preference to the form of the characteristic controlled by the allele's partner or the form of a characteristic that appears in the heterozygote

Recessive – any characteristic controlled by an allele that does not appear because the allele's partner is dominant, or any characteristic controlled by an allele that appears only in the absence of the allele's dominant partner

Genotype – the genetic make-up (all of the genes) of an individual

Phenotype – the appearance and characteristics of the cells (e.g. metabolism) of an individual resulting from those genes that are active

Genetics refers to the ways offspring inherit characteristics from their parents. The diagram shows how alleles controlling height are inherited when homozygous tall and short pea plants are crossed.

Some rules of genetics

• Paired genes controlling a particular characteristic are called alleles.

• Letters are used to symbolize alleles.

• A capital letter is used to symbolize the dominant member of a pair of alleles.

• The same letter in small print is used to symbolize the recessive member of a pair of alleles.

T symbolizes the allele that controls tall, and **t** symbolizes the allele that controls short.

Notice that the contrasting characteristic tall/short plants separates in the F_2 generation in a ratio of 3:1. Other characteristics of pea plants (e.g. flower colour) also separate in the F_2 generation in a ratio of approx. 3:1.

In the tall parent plant, both alleles which control the development of height are the same (homozygous). The parent is therefore pure breeding and produces only one kind of gamete. Every gamete carries the allele **T** which controls tallness.

In the short parent plant, both alleles which control the development of height are the same (homozygous). The parent is therefore pure breeding and produces only one kind of gamete. Every gamete carries the allele **t** which controls shortness.

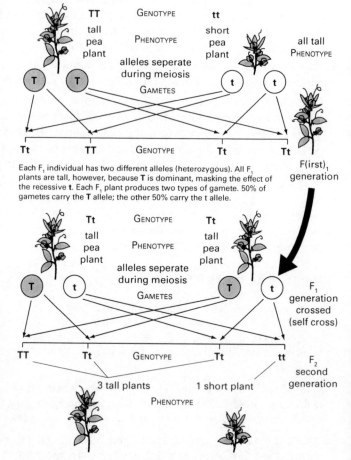

Each F_1 individual has two different alleles (heterozygous). All F_1 plants are tall, however, because **T** is dominant, masking the effect of the recessive **t**. Each F_1 plant produces two types of gamete. 50% of gametes carry the **T** allele; the other 50% carry the t allele.

Not all the tall plants have the same combination of alleles. 50% of the plants have both dominant and recessive alleles (**Tt**) (heterozygous), and 25% are pure-breeding tall (**TT**) (homozygous). The remaining 25% are pure-breeding short (**tt**) (homozygous).

The outcome of the cross allows us to state that:

• In general, when two pure-breeding individuals showing a pair of contrasting characteristics are crossed, the characteristics segregate (separate) in definite proportions in the second filial generation (F2).

Or…

• Of a pair of alleles, only one is present in a gamete. *Notice* that the outcome may be explained (as the alternative statement shows) in terms of what we know of the segregation of chromosomes at meiosis. Parental alleles separate during the formation of sex cells.

Codominance

Pea plants are either *tall* or *short*. However, some characteristics in the heterozygote are intermediate between the characteristics of the parents. For example the flowers of snap dragons may be *red* or *white*, but some may be *pink* because the alleles controlling *red* and *white* are equally dominant. The alleles are **codominant**.

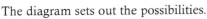

The diagram sets out the possibilities.

Notice that the letters used to symbolize the alleles controlling red (R) and white (W) are capitals. A capital letter is used to denote each allele of a codominant partnership.

In the red-flowered parent, both alleles controlling flower colour are the same (homozygous). The parent is therefore pure breeding and produces only one kind of gamete. Every gamete carries the allele **R** for redness.

In the white-flowered parent, both alleles controlling flower colour are the same (homozygous). The parent is therefore pure breeding and produces only one kind of gamete. Every gamete carries the allele **W** for whiteness.

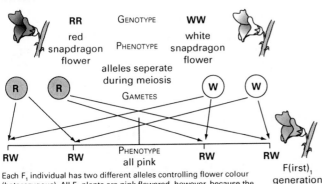

Each F_1 individual has two different alleles controlling flower colour (heterozygous). All F_1 plants are pink flowered, however, because the alleles are equally dominant. Each F_1 plant produces two types of gamete: 50% carry the **R** allele; the other 50% carry the **W** allele.

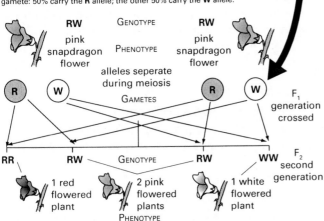

50% of plants are pure breeding (homozygous) controlling flower colour; 25% red flowered (**RR**), 25% white flowered (**WW**). The other 50% have both alleles (**RW**) and are pink flowered.

How codominant alleles controlling a characteristic (flower colour) are inherited from one generation to the next

Multiple alleles

Sometimes more than two alleles (**multiple alleles**) encode a characteristic. An individual inherits two of the alleles available. For example, the most common type of human blood group system is controlled by three alleles, A, B and O. The A and B alleles are dominant to the O allele but not to each other (they are codominant). The table sets out the possibilities. Symbols for the alleles are I^A, I^B and I^O.

Notice that if both alleles I^A and I^B are present, then the person's blood group is AB (an example of codominance). If neither allele is present, then the person's blood group is O.

Genotype(s)	Phenotype: antigen on surface of red blood cells	Blood group
$I^A I^A$ $I^A I^O$	I^A	A
$I^B I^B$ $I^B I^O$	I^B	B
$I^A I^B$	I^A and I^B	AB
$I^O I^O$	nil	O

Sex-linked inheritance

Of the 23 pairs of chromosomes in the nucleus of most human cells (e.g. a skin cell), 22 pairs are similar in size and shape in both men and women. These pairs are the **autosomes** and the alleles they carry determine the phenotype of the individual other than sex (gender). The 23rd pair is the **sex chromosomes** – **X** and **Y**. The **X** chromosome is larger than the **Y** chromosome.

- Two X chromosomes make up the sex chromosomes of a woman. We say that she is **homogametic** because the two sex chromosomes are the same and all her gametes (eggs) will be the same, each containing an X chromosome.
- The body cells of a man carry an X chromosome and a Y chromosome. He is **heterogametic** – the two sex chromosomes are different and his gametes (sperm) will be different, each containing either an X chromosome or a Y chromosome.

The X chromosome carries genes other than those which determine sex. The characteristics which these genes control are said to be **sex-linked**. There is little space on the Y chromosome for genes, other than those that determine sex. The fact that a female is homogametic means that she may be either homozygous or heterozygous for sex-linked characteristics. This is to her advantage if the characteristic is harmful, providing the gene controlling it is recessive. In the heterozygous state the recessive gene is not expressed in the phenotype. The individual is said to be a **carrier** of the harmful recessive gene.

Because a male is heterogametic, he must be homozygous for any X-linked gene (the corresponding allele which might mask the effect of its X-linked partner is not carried on the Y chromosome). As a result the X-linked gene is expressed in the phenotype.

The gene responsible for the disease **haemophilia** is an example. The diagram shows the outcome when a woman who is a carrier of the haemophilia allele becomes a mother.

One daughter is a carrier of the haemophilia gene, one son is affected by haemophilia. The other two children are not affected by haemophilia, nor is the unaffected daughter a carrier.

Questions

1. What is the difference in meaning of the terms genes and alleles?
2. Red green colour blindness is a sex-linked condition caused by a recessive allele on the X chromosome. It occurs in 8% of men but only 0.04% of women. Explain why.

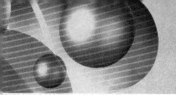

Remember

- A population is made up of a group of individuals of the same species living in the same place at the same time. A species may be represented by only one population but most have more.

- An individual's genotype is the total of all the alleles of all its genes. We can think of a population as a group of genotypes and all the alleles of all of the genes represented by the genotypes. The total of all the alleles of all the genes of a population is called a **gene pool**.

Fact file

G.H. Hardy was a prominent pure mathematician at Cambridge in the early 1900s. In 1908 the geneticist R.C. Punnett, a friend of Hardy and also at Cambridge, was puzzled by the relationship between allele frequencies and phenotype frequencies. He asked Hardy for an explanation, who promptly replied "p² to 2pq to q²". At the same time the German physician W. Weinberg came to a similar conclusion. This is why the idea is called the Hardy–Weinberg principle.

The **Hardy–Weinberg principle** states that the frequencies of alleles and genotypes in the gene pool of a population remain constant (in equilibrium) from generation to generation unless disturbed by different influences. These include:

- selection
- non-random mating
- gene flow (migration)
- small population size
- genetic drift
- mutations

One or more 'disturbing influences' always affect natural populations so Hardy–Weinberg equilibrium is only possible in laboratory conditions. For example, in small populations chance plays an important part in determining which alleles pass from parents to offspring. The probability that the frequency of alleles will be different from one generation to the next increases, the smaller the population.

- The term **genetic drift** refers to the change in the allele frequency.
- The **founder effect** which is part of your *AS level AQA Biology* is an example of genetic drift.
- A **genetic bottleneck** also covered at *AS level* may also cause genetic drift. However the idea of genetic equilibrium is useful because if provides a standard against which change in gene frequencies in natural populations can be measured. *Remember* that the extent of change in gene frequencies of a population is a measure of its rate of evolution. So, deviation from Hardy–Weinberg equilibrium indicates the evolution of a species.

Thinking it through

Think of a population with a gene that has two alleles.

- **A** – the dominant allele: p represents its frequency in the population
- **a** – the recessive allele: q represents its frequency in the population

If we assume that all members of the population carry either of the alleles or both of them…

$$p + q = 1.0 \ (100\%) \qquad \textbf{(equation 1)}$$

… the total frequency of the alleles in the population.

Equation **1** can be used to calculate the frequency of each of the alleles in the population. For example if the frequency (p) of allele **A** in the population is 0.40 (40%) then…

$$1 - 0.40 = 0.60 \ (60\%)$$

… the frequency (q) of allele a in the population.

Remember that most organisms are diploid and therefore carry the alleles of a gene in pairs. At meiosis a proportion of gametes will carry the **A** allele (frequency p); likewise a proportion of gametes will carry the **a** allele (frequency q). On fertilization the gametes combine at random to form new genotypes as:

Possible pairings		Frequency
A	A	$p \times p = p^2$
A	a	$p \times q$
a	A	$q \times p$ } $= 2pq$
a	a	$q \times q = q^2$

Notice that the frequency of:

- **AA** (homozygous) dominant genotype is p^2, and ¼ of the total possible genotypes. An individual has ¼ (25%) chance of being **AA**
- **Aa** (heterozygous) genotype is $pq + pq$ is $2pq$, and ½ of the total possible genotypes. An individual has ½ (50%) chance of being **Aa**
- **aa** (homozygous) recessive genotype is q^2, and ¼ of the total possible genotypes. An individual has ¼ (25%) chance of being **aa**

or

- homozygous dominant ¼ (25%) + heterozygous ½ (50%) + homozygous recessive ¼ (25%) = 1.0 (100% of total possible genotypes)

or

- **AA** + 2**Aa** + **aa** = 1.0 (100%)

    which may be expressed as...

- $p^2 + 2pq + q^2 = 1.0$ (100%) (**equation 2**)

    ... the **Hardy–Weinberg principle**

Put in words, the Hardy-Weinberg principle states that if the frequency of one allele (**A**) is p and the frequency of the other allele is q then...

$$p + q = 1 \text{ (equation 1)}$$

....then the frequencies of the three possible genotypes are p^2 (**AA**), $2pq$ (**Aa**) and q^2 (**aa**), so that

$$p^2 + 2pq + q^2 = 1 \text{ (equation 2)}$$

... giving, therefore, the relationship between allele frequencies and genotype frequencies.

Notice that equation 2 is equation 1 to the power^2

$$(p + q)^2 = 1$$

.... because it takes into account that most organisms are diploid.

Notice also that there are only two phenotypes:

- homozygous recessive   **aa** }
- homozygous dominant   **AA** ⎫
    heterozygous   **Aa** ⎭

.... therefore the relationship between allele frequencies and phenotype frequencies is:

frequency of the recessive phenotype = q^2

frequency of the dominant phenotype = $p^2 + 2pq$

An afterthought

It is always best to use proportions when using the Hardy–Weinberg principle rather than percentages, e.g. $2pq = 0.32$ is better than $2pq = 32\%$.

Questions

1 What is a gene pool?

2 Under what conditions will the frequencies of alleles in a gene pool remain constant?

3 Of a population of sheep, 25% have black wool. The allele controlling white wool is dominant to the allele controlling black wool. What are the frequencies of the genotypes controlling wool colour in the population?

How science works (A)

Working it through

Equations 1 and 2 can be used to calculate the frequency of any allele and genotype in a population. For example **sickle cell anaemia** is widespread in Africa and parts of India and the Mediterranean. It is caused by a recessive mutation of one of the alleles of one of the genes that control the synthesis of the oxygen absorbing pigment haemoglobin.

For the gene in question let...

Hb^A symbolize the dominant allele encoding the synthesis of normal haemoglobin

Hb^s symbolize the recessive allele encoding the synthesis of sickle haemoglobin

Asking the question...

In some parts of Africa the proportion of individuals homozygous for the recessive sickle allele is 4%. Assuming Hardy–Weinberg equilibrium, what proportion of the population would be expected to be heterozygous?

The frequency of homozygous recessives $(q^2) = 0.04$ (4% Hb^sHb^s)

Remember that ....

$p + q = 1$ (equation 1) where

p = frequency of **Hb^A**

q = frequency of **Hb^s**

... *therefore*

$q = \sqrt{(0.04)} = 0.2$

$p = 1 - 0.2 = 0.8$

... *therefore* using equation 2

$p^2 = (0.8)^2 = 0.64$ (64% **Hb^AHb^A**)

... *therefore*

$2pq = 2 \times 0.8 \times 0.2 = 0.32$ (32% **Hb^AHb^s**)

... the proportion of the population expected to be heterozygous.

So, knowing the frequency of the recessive allele **Hb^s** (q) we have been able to calculate the frequency of the dominant allele **Hb^A** (p) using equation 1. We have also been able to calculate the frequency of the three possible genotypes by taking these answers and applying them in equation 2.

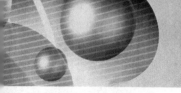

OBJECTIVES

By the end of the section you should

O *understand the concepts of gene pool and allele frequency*

O *understand the meaning of stabilizing and directional selection*

O *understand the process of speciation*

Before you start it will help to read sections **4.01** (populations), **4.03** (intraspecific competition), **4.23** (alleles), and **4.24** (gene pool).

Fact file

Present-day living things are descended from ancestors that have changed through time (evolved) over thousands of generations. The lifetime's work of the English naturalist Charles Darwin (1809–1882) provided much evidence that organisms evolve. His ideas on *how* organisms evolve were even more important. He proposed a mechanism for evolution. The mechanism is **natural selection**. In 1859 the proposal was published in his book *On the Origin of Species by Means of Natural Selection*.

Qs and As

Q Evolution is sometimes defined as a result of changes in the frequency of particular alleles. Explain the definition in terms of natural selection.

A *In the case of stabilizing selection, the frequency of alleles controlling the 'average' form of the characteristic(s) in question increases, whereas the frequency of the alleles controlling the 'extreme' forms of the characteristic decreases.*

In the case of directional selection, the frequency of the alleles controlling one of the extreme forms of the characteristic increases but the frequency of alleles controlling the 'average' form and the other 'extreme' form of the characteristic(s) decreases.

Natural selection works on the genetic variation in the gene pool. Alleles which favour survival are selected for and their **frequency** (percentage occurrence in the gene pool) changes. The characteristic(s) controlled by the favourable alleles change(s) enabling individuals with the alleles to adapt to a changing environment. The population evolves. The extent of change in the frequency of an allele (or alleles) is a measure of the rate of evolution of the population in question. Change in an environment stimulating evolution represents **selection pressure**.

Trends in natural selection

In stable environments selection pressure is low. For any particular characteristic (e.g. length of body), individuals with extremes of the characteristic (bodies which are short or long) are selected *against*. Those close to the average are selected *for* and are therefore more likely to reproduce (differential reproductive success), passing on the alleles controlling 'averageness' to the next generation. If the trend is long term, the species changes very little. Descendents, therefore, look like their distant ancestors. This kind of selection maintains the constancy of a species. It is called **stabilizing selection**.

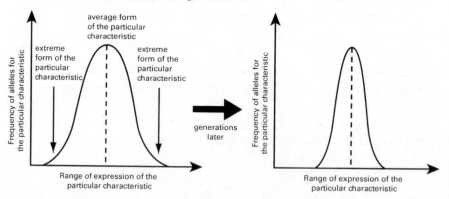

Over time, stabilizing selection reduces the frequency of the alleles for the extreme expression of a particular characteristic (e.g. length of body).

Where the environment is rapidly changing, selection pressure is high and new species quickly arise. Selection pressure promotes the adaptation of individuals to the altering circumstances.

For example, a longer body may favour survival if predators find that catching shorter bodied individuals is relatively easy. In these circumstances individuals with short bodies are selected *against* and individuals with long bodies are selected *for*. Long bodied individuals are therefore more likely to reproduce (differential reproductive success), passing on the alleles for long body to the next generation. If the trend is long term, the species changes. Descendents therefore do not look like their ancestors and become a distinct and different species. This kind of selection is called **directional selection**. Once the new characteristic is at its optimum (maximizes the survival chances of individuals) with respect to the new environment, then stabilizing selection takes over.

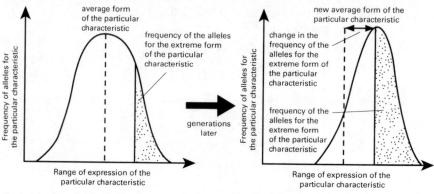

Over time directional selection increases the frequency of the alleles for an extreme expression of a characteristic (or characteristics) which become(s) the 'new average' of the evolving species.

Speciation

Speciation (the formation of new species) is the result of natural selection and the outcome of evolution. It occurs when isolating mechanisms lead to divergence of gene pools. By 'isolating mechanisms' and 'divergence of gene pools' we mean that different events interrupt the free flow of alleles from parents to offspring within the gene pool of a population.

What was a single population is separated into components each called a **deme**. The individuals of each deme encounter and respond to the slightly different circumstance of the fragmented environment, so that the process of speciation gets underway. The response over time of generations of individuals of a deme is adaptation through natural selection to the slightly different circumstances. Geographic separation brings about fragmentation of a population into demes isolated from one another.

- Separation may be local (e.g. the formation of a river or mountain range or even building a road) or large scale separation of land masses (continental drift).
  - As a result the meeting of and matings between individuals of the original population are interrupted.
  - As a result the free flow of genes is restricted to individuals of each deme.
- The individuals of each deme respond to their particular environment, which may be different from the environment encountered by the individuals living in other demes.
  - As a result the frequency of alleles in the gene pool of each deme changes differently from the gene pool of each of the other demes.
  - As a result divergence occurs as the individuals of the original population adapt within their respective deme to the environmental circumstances affecting them.
  - As a result of divergence, over time new races, sub-species and eventually new species emerge.

The term **allopatric speciation** refers to the process. The diagram shows you the idea.

The Kaibab squirrels of the north rim of the Grand Canyon Arizona, USA and the Abert squirrel of the south rim were probably one and the same species. Prolonged isolation, as a result of the barrier of the desert-like environment of the canyon floor, has given rise to the differences in colouration between individuals of the demes we see today. The different types do not interbreed and are probably two distinct species.

Kaibab squirrel

The Grand Canyon fromed as the Colorado River, flowing over sandstones and limestones eroded the soft rocks over millions of years.

The inner bark of pine trees is eaten by Kaibab squirrels.

Abert squirrel

NORTH RIM

1.6 km

SOUTH RIM

Canyon floor – pine trees do not grow in temperatures which may reach 50°C. The desert-like conditions form a barrier seaparating the squirrels of the north from squirrels of the south rim.

The inner bark of pine trees is eaten by Abert squirrels.

COLORADO RIVER

Fact file

Races or sub-species are extreme variants of a particular species. Their emergence in an environment suggests fragmentation of the environment into components each with slight differences in the conditions affecting the population of the species. These differences each represent selection pressure to which each deme responds. The emergence of races or sub-species occurs at an early stage in the process.

If then the mechanisms fragmenting the original population into demes stop having an effect, then individuals of the different races or sub species will be able to interbreed, and stabilizing selection will re-establish the *status quo*.

If however the effects of the isolating mechanisms persist, then speciation will continue and new species result. If then the isolating mechanisms cease to have an effect, stabilizing selection will not re-establish the *status quo*, as individuals of the different species will not be able to interbreed or, if they do, the offspring will probably be sterile.

Questions

1 Explain the different evolutionary outcomes of stabilizing selection and directional selection.

2 Define evolution.

3 Give examples of circumstances which fragment a population into demes.

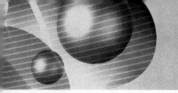

OBJECTIVES

By the end of the section you should

○ *understand that responses by organisms to stimuli increases their chances of survival*

○ *know that tropisms are responses by plants to directional stimuli*

○ *be able to describe a simple reflex arc*

Before you start it will help to read section **5.07** (neurones).

A **stimulus** is a change in the environment that causes an organism to take action. The action taken is the **response**. *Why do organisms respond to stimuli?* Improving chances of **survival** is the short answer. For example, by moving away, potential prey improve their chances of escaping predators; putting on more clothes prevents the body from becoming dangerously chilled.

The contraction of muscles pulling on a skeleton enables animals to respond to stimuli (prey moving away from a predator, for example). Plant responses are the result of growth movements. When the movements are the result of **directional stimuli** (stimuli coming mainly from one direction), then the response is called a **tropism**.

- Tropisms are **positive** if a plant grows towards the more intense source of a stimulus, and **negative** if it grows away. For example, shoots grow towards light where it is most intense (positive phototropism) and grow away from the force of gravity (negative geotropism). Roots grow to where water in the soil is most abundant (positive hydrotropism).
- As a result the plant is more likely to survive: for example, the leaves of a shoot receive as much light as possible, maximizing the rate of photosynthesis; roots 'find' water where it is most abundant.

- The tropisms (positive or negative) are the result of differences in the growth rate of tissues on one side or the other of the shoots or roots in question.

The reflex arc

Nerve impulses transmitted by **neurones (nerve cells)** carry information about stimuli (detected by **sensory receptors**) to **effectors** (muscles and glands) which respond to the stimuli.

- **Sensory neurones** ending in sensory receptor cells transmit nerve impulses to the central nervous system.
- **Relay** (or **inter-**) **neurones** link sensory neurones with motor neurones. They are within the spinal cord and the brain.
- **Motor neurones** transmit nerve impulses from the central nervous system to effectors (muscles and glands) which respond by contracting (muscles) or secreting substances (glands).

Nerves consist of bundles of hundreds/thousands of neurones. Their simplest arrangement enables an individual to respond to a stimulus. The arrangement is called a **reflex arc**. The response is a **reflex response**. We say that it is **involuntary** because it is an automatic reaction to stimuli not under conscious control. For example, we automatically jerk our hand out of harm's way if we touch a hot stove.

In the diagram, each nerve of the reflex arc is represented by only one neurone; the sensory receptor by just one receptor cell. The numbers 1–5 track the sequence of events.

Questions

1 What is a stimulus? What is a response?
2 What is the difference between a positive tropism and a negative tropism?
3 Explain why a reflex response is said to be involuntary.

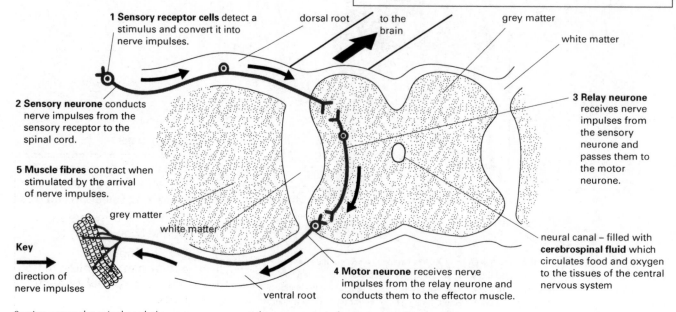

1 Sensory receptor cells detect a stimulus and convert it into nerve impulses.

dorsal root

to the brain

grey matter

white matter

2 Sensory neurone conducts nerve impulses from the sensory receptor to the spinal cord.

5 Muscle fibres contract when stimulated by the arrival of nerve impulses.

3 Relay neurone receives nerve impulses from the sensory neurone and passes them to the motor neurone.

grey matter

white matter

Key

→ direction of nerve impulses

4 Motor neurone receives nerve impulses from the relay neurone and conducts them to the effector muscle.

ventral root

neural canal – filled with **cerebrospinal fluid** which circulates food and oxygen to the tissues of the central nervous system

Section across the spinal cord: the neurones represent the arrangement of nerves which form a reflex arc.

OBJECTIVES

By the end of the section you should

○ *be able to state the similarities and differences between taxes and kineses*

○ *know how to investigate the kinetic responses of woodlice*

The word **behaviour** refers to the responses of animals to stimuli. **Taxes** and **kineses** are simple forms of behaviour. The terms describe the movements of animals (and other mobile organisms) that help them find environments where they are most likely to survive.

- Taxes (*singular* taxis) are **directional** movements which orientate an individual with respect to the stimulus causing the response.
  - **Positive (+) taxis** – an individual moves *towards* the stimulus.
  - **Negative (–) taxis** – an individual moves *away* from the stimulus.

Tactic responses are classified according to the type of stimulus, e.g. light – phototaxis; chemicals – chemotaxis.

- Kineses (*singular* kinesis) are random **non-directional** movements: an individual does not move towards or away from a stimulus but
  - moves faster
  - changes direction more frequently

  … in response to the intensity of a stimulus which threatens its survival. The more intense the threatening stimulus, the faster are the movements and the more frequent the changes of direction.

  In this way the individual is more likely to find quickly a less threatening environment. The movements then slow and may stop altogether, and so the individual spends more time in an environment where it is more likely to survive. Like taxes, kinetic responses are classified according to the type of stimulus, e.g. photokinesis.

Examples

- Maggots (fly larvae) and woodlice quickly lose water from the body in dry air, threatening their survival. The air of open, brightly lit habitats is likely to be drier than the air of shaded, dimly lit habitats.
  - As a result maggots and woodlice are more likely to be found in dimly lit habitats where air is **humid** (saturated with water vapour).
  - As a result, loss of water from the body is reduced.
  - As a result maggots and woodlice are more likely to survive.

How do maggots and woodlice find dimly lit habitats?

- Maggots are negatively phototactic: they move away from bright light.
  - As a result they move towards dim light.
  - As a result they are more likely to survive in the humid air associated with dimly lit habitats.

- Woodlice are photokinetic: they move faster and change direction more frequently the brighter (more intense) the light (and therefore the drier the air).
  - As a result, the more active woodlice are more likely to find a dimly lit habitat where the air is more likely to be humid.
- Woodlice are much less active in dimly lit habitats.
  - As a result they are more likely to remain in dimly lit habitats and survive.

How science works (D)

Investigating photokinesis

You can use a **choice chamber** to investigate the responses of woodlice to dry/humid and light/dark environments. The diagram gives you the idea. Remember that the responses of woodlice are an example of photokinesis.

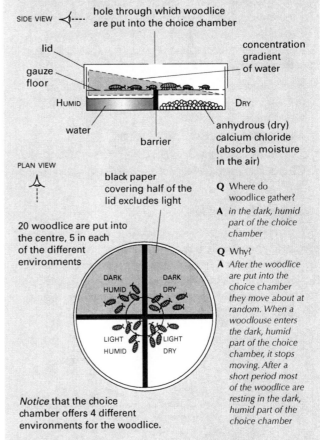

Notice that the choice chamber offers 4 different environments for the woodlice.

Q Where do woodlice gather?

A *in the dark, humid part of the choice chamber*

Q Why?

A *After the woodlice are put into the choice chamber they move about at random. When a woodlouse enters the dark, humid part of the choice chamber, it stops moving. After a short period most of the woodlice are resting in the dark, humid part of the choice chamber*

The choice chamber allows woodlice to find and remain in an environment which favours their survival.

Questions

1 Explain the difference between taxes and kineses.

2 Briefly summarize how maggots and woodlice find habitats where they are more likely to survive.

3 Describe how you set up an investigation into the responses of woodlice to dry/humid and light/dark environments.

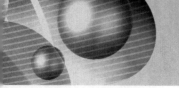

5.03　Sensory receptors

A sensory receptor is the part of the dendrite of a sensory neurone which detects stimuli. It is the first link in the chain of events that brings about a response. The cells of sensory receptors are biological **transducers**, converting one form of energy (the stimulus) into electrical energy (action potentials) to which the body can respond. Animal sensory receptors are categorized according to the stimuli they detect.

- **Mechanoreceptors** detect physical force such as pressure and stretch (touch, muscle contraction/ relaxation).
- **Photoreceptors** detect light (vision).
- **Thermoreceptors** detect changes in temperature.
- **Chemoreceptors** detect substances in solution (taste/ smell).

Pacinian corpuscles

Lying deep within the skin, **Pacinian corpuscles** detect pressure when the skin is firmly touched. They are mechanoreceptors. Each contains the single end of the nerve fibre of a dendrite of a sensory neurone, wrapped around by layers of membrane called **lamellae**. A jelly-like material separates the layers.

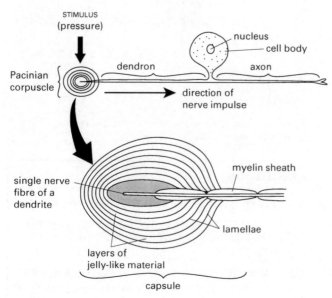

A sensory neurone and its Pacinian corpuscle. The sensory dendrite is enclosed by layers of lamellae forming a capsule.

The pressure of a firm touch (stimulus) deforms (stretches and changes the shape of) the capsule of a Pacinian corpuscle. The pressure must be enough to deform the dendrite as well as the capsule.

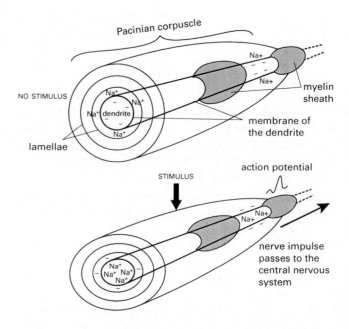

- At rest the concentration of sodium ions (Na^+) on the outer surface of the membrane of the dendrite is greater than the inner surface.
- Deformation of a localized part of the membrane temporarily alters its permeability to Na^+.
  - As a result Na^+ diffuses down its concentration gradient from the outer surface to the inner surface of the membrane.
  - As a result the inner surface becomes less negatively charged. We say that the membrane is **depolarized**.
- Localized depolarization in a Pacinian corpuscle (and other sensory receptor cells) is called a **generator potential**.
- The more intense (stronger) the stimulus, the greater is the generator potential.
- When the generator potential reaches (or is more than) a threshold value, it triggers an action potential in the sensory neurone attached to the Pacinian corpuscle.

Rods and cones

Cells called **rods** and **cones** line the retina of the human eye. The cells are photoreceptors. They convert light energy into the electrical energy of generator potentials. Rods and cones are connected to a network of other neurones in the retina. These neurones form the fibres of the optic nerve, which passes from each eye to the visual cortex of the brain. The generator potentials formed in the rods and cones trigger action potentials in each optic nerve. The action potentials are transmitted as nerve impulses along each optic nerve to the visual cortex. Here they are interpreted as images of the object we are looking at.

The connections between rods, cones, and the other neurones in the retina are shown in the diagram.

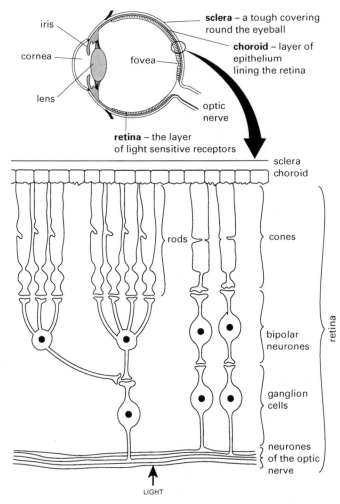

- There are about 120 million rods in each retina. Rods are mostly found at the edges of the retina. They are only sensitive to low intensity light.
- There are about 6 million cones in each retina.
- Cones are densely packed in the middle of the retina, particularly in the region called the **fovea** (yellow spot). They are only sensitive to high intensity light.

In the diagram the other neurones in the retina are **bipolar neurones** and **ganglion cells**.

Notice:

- A number of rod cells synapse with…
  - one bipolar neurone. A number of bipolar neurones synapse with…
  - one ganglion cell

  The arrangement is called **convergence**.
- Only one cone cell synapses with…
  - one bipolar neurone, which synapses with…
  - one ganglion cell

Overall the degree of convergence for cones is much less than rods. Usually the relationship between cones, bipolar neurones, and ganglion cells is 1:1:1.

Sensitivity and visual acuity

Sensitivity refers to the intensity of light required to stimulate rods and cones. Convergence increases sensitivity.

- *Remember* that a number of rods synapse with a single bipolar neurone and that many bipolar neurones synapse with one ganglion cell.
  - As a result the generator potentials from the rods are 'pooled' and generate action potentials in the ganglion cell connected to the bipolar neurones.
- Nerve impulses are transmitted along each optic nerve to the visual cortex of the brain.
  - As a result we 'see' in dim light.
- The 'pooling' of generator potentials is an example of **summation**.
- Without summation, the generator potentials of a single rod would not be sufficient to trigger action potentials in a ganglion cell.
  - As a result we would not 'see' in dim light.
- *Remember* that rods are found mostly at the edges of the retina.
  - As a result seeing in dim light is best at the edges of the field of vision (looking at objects out of the sides of the eyes).

Visual acuity refers to the sharpness (detail) of the image we see. If we see closely placed points as ●●● then we say that the cells of the retina have **resolved** the points as separate images. In this case, our acuity is greater than if we see the points as ●●. The points are not resolved.

- Convergence reduces acuity.
  - As a result rods do not give such high resolution as cones.

Remember that cones are only sensitive to high intensity light. Cones mostly each synapse with only one bipolar neurone, which in turn synapses with only one ganglion cell. The 1:1:1 relationship means that:

- Each part of an image is detected by a separate cell.
- There is no 'pooling' of generator potentials.
  - As a result detail is not lost… why?
- The information of the generator potentials (and therefore the nerve impulses transmitted along each optic nerve) is not combined.
  - As a result the details of an image are resolved and the image is sharp.
- *Remember* that cones are found mostly in the middle of the retina at the fovea.
  - As a result seeing in bright light is best at the centre of the field of vision (looking at objects straight ahead).

Questions

1 Why are sensory receptors biological transducers?

2 How does a firm touch trigger an action potential in the sensory neurone attached to a Pacinian corpuscle?

3 With reference to the rods and cones of the retina of the eye, briefly summarize the meaning of **convergence**, **summation**, and **visual acuity**.

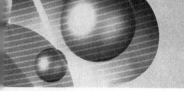
By the end of the section you should

○ *understand how chemoreceptors, pressure receptors, the autonomic nervous system, and effectors control heart rate*

○ *know the consequences of the effect of adrenaline on heart rate*

Before you start it will help to read sections **5.03** (receptors), **5.05** (hormones), and **5.13** (negative feedback).

The **heart rate** is measured as the number of ventricular contractions per minute. Usually we think of the contractions as the heart beat.

Recall from your work at *AS level* that the sino-atrial node (SAN) is located in the wall of the right atrium of the heart. Tissue in the SAN, called the **pacemaker**, determines a spontaneous average heart rate of about 100 beats per minute. The average heart rate of a healthy person at rest is about 72 beats per minute. Nervous and hormonal control of the heart rate accounts for the difference in the figures. The diagram represents connections between the brain, different receptors, and the SAN. Together, they help to control the heart rate.

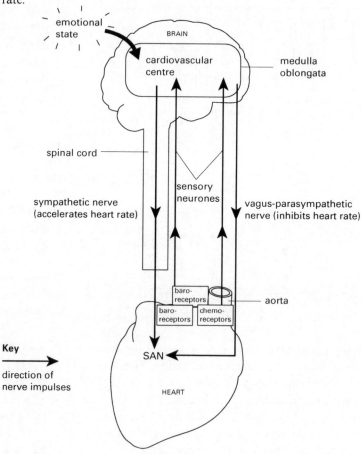

Notice:

- The **cardiovascular centre** is located in the part of the brain called the **medulla oblongata**.
- The **sympathetic nerve** and **vagus nerve** lead from the cardiovascular centre to the pacemaker in the SAN. The nerves are part of the **autonomic nervous system** which controls the involuntary (unconscious) actions of the body. *Recall* that the autonomic nervous system consists of sympathetic nerves and parasympathetic nerves.
- The sympathetic nerve passes from the cardiovascular centre to the pacemaker via the spinal cord.
- The vagus nerve is a parasympathetic nerve. It passes from the cardiovascular centre directly to the pacemaker.
- **Baroreceptors** are located in a swelling of the carotid artery called the **carotid sinus**, and in the walls of the heart.
- **Chemoreceptors** are located in the
  - ○ glandular tissue of the **carotid body** near to the carotid artery, branching from the aorta
  - ○ aorta
  - ○ walls of the heart
  - ○ medulla oblongata of the brain

Nervous control of heart rate

Baroreceptors are a type of mechanoreceptor. They detect changes in pressure. Here they detect changes in blood pressure. The chemoreceptors are sensitive to changes in pH and concentrations of carbon dioxide and oxygen in the blood.

This sensory information passes as nerve impulses via sensory neurones to the cardiovascular centre in the medulla oblongata of the brain. The information is processed in the medulla oblongata, stimulating the sympathetic nerve and the vagus nerve. *Recall* that these nerves pass from the medulla oblongata to the pacemaker in the SAN.

Nerve impulses transmitted to the pacemaker by the

- sympathetic nerve *accelerate* heart rate
- vagus nerve *inhibit* heart rate

The effect of the sympathetic nerve on the pacemaker opposes the effect of the vagus nerve. We say that the effects are **antagonistic**. A person's actual heart rate depends on the balance of activity between the nerves.

Recall that the spontaneous average heart rate is about 100 beats per minute. This means that the average resting heart rate of 72 beats per minute is set by the activity of the vagus nerve.

Heart rate varies

Age, gender, and fitness affect the resting heart rate. On average at rest, a child's heart rate is faster than an adult's, an adult woman's heart rate is faster than that of a man's, and the heart rate of an endurance athlete is likely to be slowest of all.

Exercise affects heart rate irrespective of age, gender, or fitness and increases in proportion to the intensity of the activity and the individual's oxygen uptake. It leads to

- an increase in concentration of carbon dioxide in the blood
- a decrease in blood pH
- The changes are detected by the chemoreceptors in the locations listed above.
- The sensory information passes to the cardiovascular centre.
    - As a result the sympathetic nerve is stimulated and nerve impulses pass to the pacemaker.
    - As a result the heart rate increases.
    - As a result the output of blood from the heart (cardiac output) increases.
    - As a result more blood with its load of carbon dioxide passes to the lungs.
    - As a result more carbon dioxide is exhaled.
    - As a result the concentration of carbon dioxide in the blood decreases.
    - As a result stimulation of the pacemaker by nerve impulses from the sympathetic nerve decreases.
    - As a result heart rate returns to normal.

Notice that the process is an example of **negative feedback** which regulates the concentration of carbon dioxide in the blood (and its pH, and indirectly its oxygen concentration) and therefore the heart rate.

Hormones also affect heart rate. **Adrenaline** is released by the sympathetic nervous system in response to a person's emotional state (excitement, fear).

- Adrenaline increases the heart rate.
    - As a result more oxygen and nutrients reach the muscles.
    - As a result more glucose is available, enabling muscle cells to respire more rapidly and produce more ATP.
    - As a result more energy resources are available, enabling muscles to contract more vigorously.
    - As a result the individual is able to respond quickly to the stimulus which triggered the sequence of events in the first place.

Because of the consequences of its activity, adrenaline is sometimes called the 'flight or fight' hormone.

Questions

1 How are the sympathetic nerve and vagus nerve antagonistic to one another?

2 Briefly describe the role of sensory receptors in the control of the heart rate.

3 What is the result of the effect of adrenaline on the heart rate?

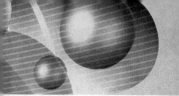

5.05 Electrical and chemical coordination

An individual's coordinated responses to changes in the environment (stimuli) are the result of the coordinated activities of the nervous system and endocrine system. Although their activities may be coordinated, the two systems work in different ways.

Nervous system	Endocrine system
• **Nerve impulses** are electrical and transmitted by nerve cells called **neurones**.	• **Hormones** are chemicals produced by different **endocrine glands** which secrete them into the bloodstream.
• Muscles or glands (called **effectors**) respond to nerve impulses.	• Hormones are transported in the bloodstream to all parts of the body. However, each hormone only affects its particular **target tissue** because only that tissue has receptors which bind to the hormone in question.
• Effectors respond to nerve impulses in milliseconds.	• The response of a target tissue to its particular hormone is long-lasting.

Nerves and the nervous system

Neurones are grouped into bundles called **nerves** which pass to all of the muscles and glands (the effectors) of the body. The nerves form the **nervous system**:

• the **central nervous system** consists of the brain and spinal (nerve) cord
• the **peripheral nervous system** consists of the cranial nerves and spinal nerves joining the central nervous system.

The diagram illustrates the arrangement.

If an individual's response to a stimulus is controlled by the brain it is called a **voluntary** response. Thinking and decision are part of the process. If thinking and decision are not involved then the response is said to be **involuntary**. A **reflex response** is involuntary.

The **autonomic nervous system** controls involuntary responses: for example, movement of the gut and the release of some of its internal secretions, breathing movements, and the beating of the heart. It forms part of the peripheral nervous system and consists of the **sympathetic nervous system** and the **parasympathetic nervous system**.

Sympathetic nervous system	Parasympathetic nervous system
• raises blood pressure	• reduces blood pressure
• raises the output of blood from the heart	• reduces the output of blood from the heart
• raises the rate of ventilation	• reduces the rate of ventilation
• dilates the pupil of the eye	• narrows the pupil of the eye

Comparing some effects of the sympathetic nervous system and the parasympathetic nervous system

Notice that the effects of the sympathetic nervous system oppose the effects of the parasympathetic nervous system. We say that the effects are **antagonistic**. The balance of antagonistic effects regulates the involuntary responses of muscles and glands. Control of heart rate is an example.

Fact file

Not all effects of the sympathetic and parasympathetic nervous system are antagonistic. For example, the sympathetic system stimulates sweating. However, the parasympathetic system has no comparable effect.

central nervous system

brain

cranial nerves

spinal (nerve) cord

peripheral nervous system

spinal nerves

The human nervous system

Hormones and endocrine glands

The blood system is the link between a hormone and its target tissue. The sequence reads:

Hormones are chemical messengers synthesized in **endocrine glands** and secreted directly into the capillary vessels which supply blood to each gland. This is why endocrine glands are called **ductless glands** (hormone is not secreted through a duct, or tube, to its target tissue). The diagram shows where endocrine glands are located in the body.

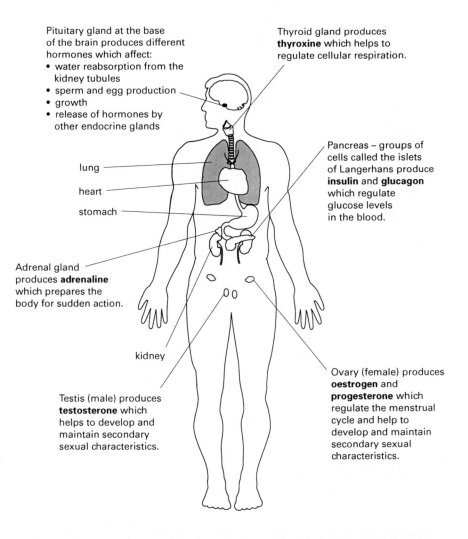

Pituitary gland at the base of the brain produces different hormones which affect:
• water reabsorption from the kidney tubules
• sperm and egg production
• growth
• release of hormones by other endocrine glands

lung

heart

stomach

Adrenal gland produces **adrenaline** which prepares the body for sudden action.

kidney

Testis (male) produces **testosterone** which helps to develop and maintain secondary sexual characteristics.

Thyroid gland produces **thyroxine** which helps to regulate cellular respiration.

Pancreas – groups of cells called the islets of Langerhans produce **insulin** and **glucagon** which regulate glucose levels in the blood.

Ovary (female) produces **oestrogen** and **progesterone** which regulate the menstrual cycle and help to develop and maintain secondary sexual characteristics.

Fact file

A gland consists of a cluster of cells which produces and secretes (releases) one or more substances with widespread effects. The substance(s) produced is the secretion. The action of most hormones is long-lasting. The exception is adrenaline which rapidly prepares the body for sudden action.

Local chemical mediators

Like hormones, **local chemical mediators** carry information. Unlike hormones they are not transported in the blood to target tissues elsewhere in the body, but affect the cells that synthesize them or cells nearby. **Histamine** and **prostaglandins** are examples of local chemical mediators.

• Histamine is released in response to the localized presence of an antigen (a substance which the body does not recognize as its own): the poison of a singing nettle for example. It is produced by **white blood cells** and **mast cells** which are found in connective tissue. Its effects include pain, heat, redness, and inflammation. We say that the effect is a **non-specific immune response** because histamine is released in response to many different antigens, not just a particular antigen.

• There are about 30 different prostaglandins synthesized from fatty acids by most types of cells throughout the body. Their functions are various and often with opposite effects depending on the types of prostaglandin. For example, depending on type, some promote or inhibit
  ○ the body's inflammatory responses
  ○ blood clotting
  ○ contraction of the muscles of the wall of the intestine

Other prostaglandins induce (bring on) labour, which begins the birth process, relax the muscles in the walls of blood vessels reducing blood pressure, and increase blood flow in the kidneys.

Ibuprofen and aspirin reduce inflammation. *Why?* The drugs inhibit the secretion of prostaglandins.

Questions

1 The nervous system and endocrine system work in different ways. Summarize the differences.

2 How are local chemical mediators different from hormones?

3 Why does aspirin reduce inflammation?

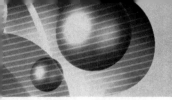

OBJECTIVES

By the end of the section you should

○ *know that in flowering plants responses are often the result of movements brought about by growth*

○ *understand that substances called growth factors control growth movements*

○ *understand the role of indoleacetic acid (IAA) in controlling tropisms in flowering plants*

Before you start it will help to read section **5.01** (tropism).

Recall that in flowering plants, many of their responses to stimuli are movements which are the result of growth. Stimuli which are more intense from one direction are called **directional stimuli**. For example, light shining from a particular direction (unidirectional) stimulates shoots to bend and grow towards it. Growth movements in response to directional stimuli are called **tropisms**.

How science works (H)

Discovering indoleacetic acid (IAA)

In 1928, the Dutch plant biologist Frits Went investigated the response of seedlings to unidirectional light. The results of his experiments suggested that a substance

• is produced in the tips of coleoptiles
• passes to the region behind the tip
• stimulates growth so that the coleoptiles grow towards unidirectional light.

Went found that the extent to which coleoptiles grow towards directional light is proportional to the amount of substance present. His observation is an example of biological measurement as a result of **bioassay**. The technique allows comparison of the effect of an unknown amount of a substance with the effect that samples of known amounts of the substance have on a biological system (in this case the angle of bending of coleoptiles to directional light). The diagram shows you the idea.

1 A coleoptile is decapitated and the tip placed on top of a block of agar.

2 The block of agar is placed on one side of the decapitated coleoptile.

3 The decapitated coleoptile bends over. The angle at which it bends is measured.

The bending of the coleoptile suggests that the increase in concentration of the substance in the tissues of one side of the coleoptile promotes growth on that side. As a result the coleoptile bends over.

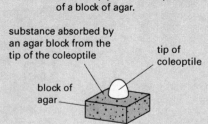
substance absorbed by an agar block from the tip of the coleoptile

tip of coleoptile

block of agar

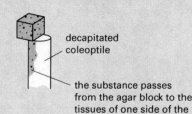
decapitated coleoptile

the substance passes from the agar block to the tissues of one side of the decapitated coleoptile.

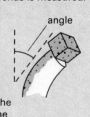
angle

The substance that Went collected was called **auxin** (from the Greek word auxein, 'to grow'). In 1934, auxin was identified as **indoleacetic acid** (IAA). It is widely distributed in plant tissues and regulates their growth.

Fact file

The coleoptile is a sheath of tissue which encloses the shoot of a germinating grass seedling. It grows like a shoot. Its uncluttered structure makes its growth easier to observe.

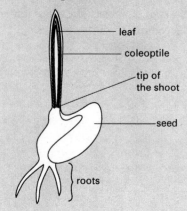
— leaf

— coleoptile

— tip of the shoot

— seed

roots

How science works (B)

How does IAA work?

Following Went's investigations it was found that IAA loosens the bundling of the cellulose fibres of the cell wall. In the early 1970s, several research teams demonstrated that loosening is partly the result of a lowering of pH of the environment outside of the affected cells. The increasing acidity of the environment is due to IAA stimulating cells to secrete protons (H^+).

The affected cells also maintain a low internal water potential. Water therefore enters the cell by osmosis and the increase in hydrostatic pressure causes the cells to elongate, helped by the more loosely bound framework of cellulose fibres in the cell walls.

If the elongation of cells occurs on one side of the shoot only, then the shoot curves. Curvature is not only due to cell elongation but also the result of growth which in part depends on the synthesis of cell wall materials.

Phototropism, geotropism, and auxin

IAA is synthesized in young leaves and the tips of shoots. A small amount may also be synthesized in the tips of roots. Its transport is by

- diffusion from cell to cell
- translocation in the phloem from shoots to roots

Elongation of cells is either *stimulated* or *inhibited* depending on the concentration of IAA and its location in plant tissues. The graph and diagram show you the idea.

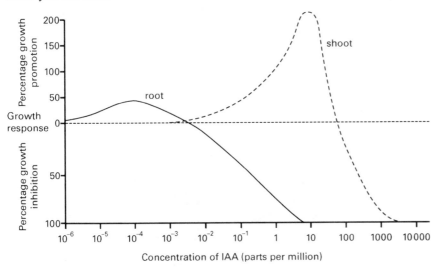

Growth of shoot and root in response to the concentration of IAA. The scale for IAA concentration is logarithmic.

Notice that the concentration of IAA which stimulates the growth of shoots also inhibits the growth of roots. The diagram illustrates the outcome of the different responses.

Research shows that, in seedlings, auxin accumulates on the shaded side of a shoot tip illuminated by directional light. The faster elongation of cells on the shaded side compared with the brightly lit side results in curvature of the shoot towards the light source.

In the root tip of seedlings, accumulation of auxin on the lower side produces an opposite response. The elongation of cells is inhibited while the cells on the upper side elongate faster, with the result that the root grows downwards. Downward growth occurs even if the root of the seedling is exposed to light. In other words, roots are negatively phototropic and positively geotropic as the diagram above illustrates.

Other roles of IAA

IAA is not only associated with the tropic responses of plants. It is also responsible for other aspects of plant growth. *Remember* that the action of IAA as a promoter or inhibitor of growth depends on its concentration and the tissue in question.

- **Apical dominance** – IAA present in the tip of the shoot apex (the top of the shoot) inhibits cell division in the lateral (side) buds below, preventing the growth of lateral shoots. The term apical dominance refers to the relationship between the apex and lateral buds of a shoot. Lopping of the shoot apex removes the source of IAA and side shoots develop. This is why a gardener trims a hedge to make it more bushy.
- **Growth of lateral roots** – cells in the pericycle of the root are stimulated by IAA to divide. (*Recall* learning about the pericycle at *AS level*.) Lateral (side) roots develop.
- **Leaf fall** – IAA is highly concentrated in young leaves. It inhibits their fall by preventing formation of the layer of tissue (called the **abscission layer**) which develops at the base of the stalk of older leaves before they fall from the plant. The abscission layer forms because the concentration of IAA in leaves declines as they age.

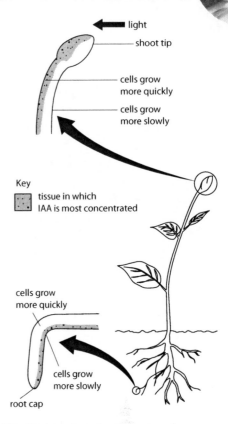

IAA stimulates elongation in shoots and inhibits it in roots.

Other growth regulators and their interactions

After IAA was isolated other growth regulators were soon discovered. Today we know that a range of substances regulate different aspects of plant growth. The substances include **gibberellins**, **cytokinins**, **abscisic acid**, and **ethene**.

The responses of plants to stimuli are often the result of the interactions between the different growth factors. If one factor enhances the effect of another then the interaction is stimulatory. We say it is **synergistic**. If the effect of a factor is reduced by another, then the interaction is inhibitory. We say it is **antagonistic**. Overall plant responses are the result of the balance between synergistic and antagonistic effects of the growth factors.

> ## Questions
>
> 1 How does IAA work?
> 2 What is a bioassay?
> 3 Use the internet to find out how gibberellins, cytokinins, abscisic acid, and ethene regulate different aspects of plant growth.

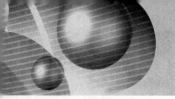

The neurone

Recall that each nerve of the nervous system consists of a bundle of neurones. The diagram shows a human motor neurone.

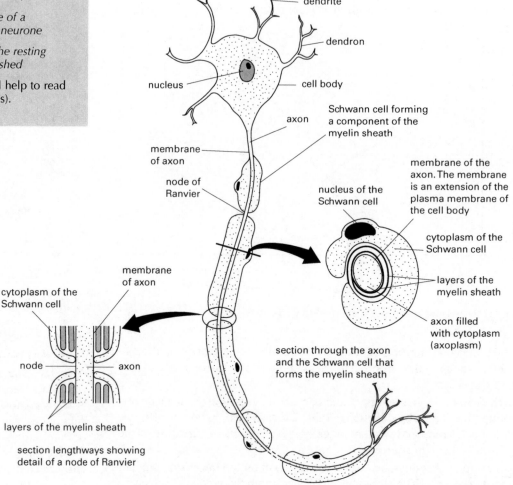

- A **dendron** and its **dendrites** are thin extensions of the **cell body** which carry nerve impulses *towards* the cell body.
- **Axon** – an extension of the cell body that carries nerve impulses *away* from the cell body.
- **Schwann cell** – a type of cell that forms the components of the myelin sheath during the development of the nervous system.
- **Myelin sheath** – forms from Schwann cells. It consists of layers of membrane wrapped round the axon. Myelin is a fatty substance and an important component of the sheath. It insulates the axon.
- **Node of Ranvier** – a break in the myelin sheath where the axon is uncovered. Nerve impulses jump from node to node, speeding up their passage along the axon.

Resting potential

Remember that the axon is an extension of the cell body of a neurone. It is surrounded by a membrane which is an extension of the plasma membrane surrounding the cell body.

The diagram shows the distribution of ions on either side of the membrane of the axon of a neurone at rest (not stimulated). The concentrations of

- sodium ions (Na^+) is higher on the outer surface of the membrane than on the inner surface
- potassium ions (K^+) is higher on the inner surface of the membrane than on its outer surface

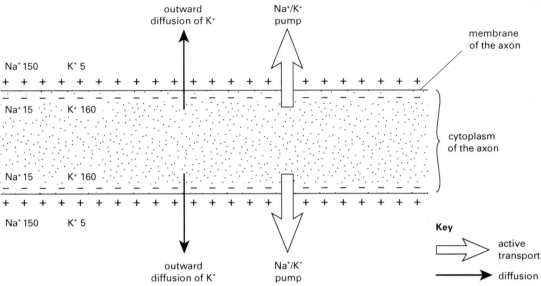

The figures on the outer surface and inner surface of the membrane of the axon are a measure of the concentration of ions.

The distribution of ions on both sides of the membrane of an axon at rest

Since the concentration of potassium ions is much greater on the inner surface of the membrane compared with the outer surface, potassium ions rapidly diffuse out of the axon. Remember that potassium ions are positively charged, (K^+). The outward diffusion of positive ions, therefore, means that the inner surface of the membrane becomes slightly negative relative to its outer surface.

As more potassium ions pass to the outer surface of the membrane, their diffusion outwards slows until equilibrium is reached. At this point the rate of diffusion of potassium ions out of and into the axon across its membrane is balanced.

How is the difference in concentration of the different ions across the membrane maintained? Active transport makes the difference.

- Sodium ions and potassium ions are actively exchanged by the **sodium–potassium pump** located in the membrane of the axon. Recall that covering the action of the pump is part of the specification of Unit 2 (*AS level*). *Remember* that for every three sodium ions removed from the axon by the sodium–potassium pump, two potassium ions are brought in.

  - As a result there are more positive ions on the outer surface of the membrane than on its inner surface.

  - As a result the negativity of the inner surface of the membrane established by the outward diffusion of potassium ions is maintained.

The difference (electrical potential of the inner surface of the membrane of the axon – the electrical potential of its outer surface) is called the **potential difference** and is usually about –65 mV. The value represents the **resting potential** of the membrane and overall the axon is said to be **polarized**.

Fact file

A resting potential of –65 mV means that the electrical potential of the inner surface of the membrane of the axon is 65 mV lower than the outer surface. Accumulation of negatively charged organic ions (mostly of the amino acids aspartate and glutamate) along the inner surface of the membrane helps to maintain its negativity. The ions do not diffuse out of the axon because its membrane is impermeable to them.

Qs and As

Q Why do many more potassium ions diffuse out of the axon than sodium ions diffuse in?

A *The membrane of the axon is much more permeable to potassium ions than sodium ions.*

Questions

1 What is the relationship between Schwann cells and the myelin sheath wrapped round the axon of a neurone?

2 Explain how the resting potential of an axon is maintained.

3 What is the difference between a dendron and an axon?

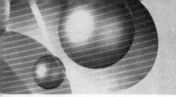

OBJECTIVES

By the end of the section you should

○ *be able to explain that changes in membrane permeability lead to the generation of an action potential*

○ *understand the importance of the refractory period*

○ *know which factors affect the speed of conductance of nerve impulses*

Before you start it will help to read section **5.07** (resting potential), and **5.09** (voltage gated).

The diagram shows that the potential difference across the membrane of the axon of a stimulated neurone changes. The change in potential difference reverses the resting potential and is called an **action potential**.

An action potential: the trace shows resting and action potentials recorded by a cathode ray oscilloscope (the instrument is used to measure small electrical changes). The changes in the movement of ions across the membrane of the axon correspond to the trace. Notice that the nerve impulse is moving from right to left.

Fact file

The channels in the membrane which allow the passage of sodium ions and potassium ions are closed when the membrane is in its resting state (polarized). When the membrane is depolarized they open, allowing the passage of ions. The channels are said to be **voltage- gated** because they open only when the potential difference of the membrane of the axon changes following a stimulus.

The fact that the sodium channels open more quickly than the potassium channels accounts for the

• *depolarization* of the membrane when sodium ions enter the axon

• *repolarization* of the membrane when potassium ions leave the axon

• The action of the sodium–potassium pump in the membrane of the axon stops.

  ◉ As a result the permeability of the membrane to sodium ions and potassium ions changes. Ion channels open in the membrane and the ions diffuse along their respective concentration gradients produced when the axon was at rest.

• Sodium channels are the first to open. Sodium ions diffuse from where they are in greater concentration on the outer surface of the membrane to the inner surface where they are in lower concentration.

  ◉ As a result the inner surface of the membrane becomes less negative. We say that the membrane is **depolarized**.

• Positive charge builds up on the inner surface of the membrane as sodium ions continue to diffuse into the axon.

• When the electrical potential of the inner surface of the membrane reaches +40 mV compared with the outer surface, the sodium channels close.

  ◉ As a result sodium ions stop diffusing into the axon.

• Potassium channels in the membrane then open. Potassium ions diffuse from where they are in greater concentration on the inner surface of the membrane to the outer surface where they are in lower concentration.

  ◉ As a result the inner surface of the membrane becomes more negative. We say that the membrane is **repolarized**.

- Potassium ions continue to diffuse from the inner surface of the membrane to its outer surface. This diffusion makes the potential difference across the membrane even more negative than the resting potential of –65 mV (**hyperpolarization**). Checking the diagram shows you what happens.
- Activity of the sodium–potassium pump in the axon membrane is restored.
  - As a result the distribution of sodium ions and potassium ions along the outer and inner surface of the membrane is restored.
  - As a result the potential difference across the membrane is restored to its resting state of –65 mV.

Recovery

The removal of potassium ions from the axon marks the beginning of the recovery phase. The membrane of the axon behind the action potential is repolarized and its resting potential restored. Reactivation of the sodium–potassium pump completes the process.

The period of recovery is called the **refractory period**. It lasts for about 1 ms, during which the generation of new action potentials is not possible. As a result the refractory period

- determines the **frequency** (number per unit time) with which action potentials are transmitted along the axon
- the direction of the action potentials, i.e. *from* the cell body to the end of its axon. Action potentials cannot travel in the opposite direction because the membrane behind the action potential is refractory during the restoration of its resting potential.

Transmission of action potentials

Notice in the diagram the leading edge of the depolarized region of the membrane. Here **local circuits** cause depolarization of the resting part of the membrane ahead of the action potential. In this way the action potential moves (is **conducted**) along the axon. The conduction of an action potential is the **nerve impulse**.

The speed of conduction depends on the

- *myelin sheath* – its presence speeds up conduction
- *diameter of the axon* – the greater it is, the greater is the speed of conduction.

Axons covered with myelin are said to be **myelinated**. The fatty component of myelin electrically insulates the axon. *Remember* that the myelin sheath of a neurone is constricted at intervals along its length. Each constriction is called a **node of Ranvier**. The myelin sheath is broken and the axon uncovered.

Depolarization and the formation of action potentials cannot take place where the axon is myelinated. However action potentials can form at the nodes of Ranvier. Action potentials therefore jump from node to node (called **saltatory conduction**) speeding up their conduction. The speed of conduction reaches 120 m s^{-1} for some myelinated axons compared with 0.5 m s^{-1} for non-myelinated ones.

Action potentials only form if the stimulus is strong enough to begin depolarization of the membrane of the axon. In other words the stimulus must have a **threshold** value. A sub-threshold stimulus on its own is ineffective but a series quickly repeated may have a cumulative effect sufficient to initiate an action potential. The process is called **summation**.

Once started, the amplitude of the action potential remains the same at +40 mV as it travels along an axon, regardless of the strength of the stimulus above its threshold value. In other words, the formation of an action potential is an **all-or-nothing** response.

Qs and As

Q Why is the generation of new action potentials not possible during the refractory period?

A *Hyperpolarization at the beginning of the refractory period makes the generation of new action potentials impossible no matter how intense the stimulus.*

Why? The sodium channels are closed and depolarization cannot take place.

Qs and As

Q Why is an action potential an all-or-nothing response regardless of the strength of a stimulus above its threshold value?

A *The depolarization and repolarization of the membrane of an axon depends on the concentration gradients of sodium ions and potassium ions, and the timing of the openings of the voltage-gated ion channels. The concentration gradients and timings are fixed so the size of the action potential is constant, regardless of the strength of a stimulus above its threshold value.*

Questions

1 How does an axon become depolarized?
2 What is hyperpolarization?
3 Briefly explain the outcomes of the refractory period on the transmission of nerve impulses.

The synapse

The axon of a neurone ends in swellings called **synaptic knobs**. A minute gap called the **synapse** separates the knobs from the dendrites of the next neurone in line. Each knob contains numerous mitochondria and structures called **synaptic vesicles**. The membrane round a synaptic knob is called the **pre-synaptic** membrane. The membrane of a dendrite of the next neurone in line is called the **post-synaptic** membrane. In between each membrane is the narrow gap of the **synaptic cleft**. The gap is about 10 nm wide. Information must pass across each synapse from one neurone to the next for effectors to be able to respond to stimuli. The transmission of information across most synapses is chemical.

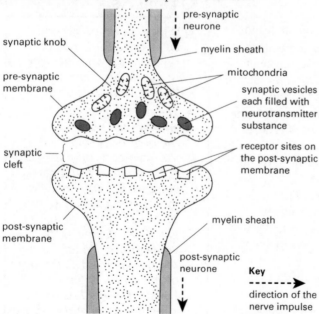

The structure of a synapse – acetylcholine molecules bind with the receptor sites on the post-synaptic membrane because the shape of molecule and receptor match.

The diagram illustrates the structure of a chemical synapse. The synaptic vesicles each contains the chemical which diffuses across the synapse. The chemical is called **neurotransmitter** substance. **Acetylcholine** is an example of neurotransmitter substance. Neurones whose synapses depend on acetylcholine are called **cholinergic** neurones.

Transmission across the synapse

- The arrival of an action potential at a synaptic knob opens calcium channels in its pre-synaptic membrane, making it more permeable to calcium ions (Ca^{2+}) present in the synaptic cleft. We say that the channels are **voltage gated**.

- The calcium ions rapidly diffuse into the synaptic knob. They cause the synaptic vesicles filled with molecules of acetylcholine to move to the pre-synaptic membrane and fuse with it. The vesicles empty (an example of exocytosis) acetylcholine into the synaptic cleft.

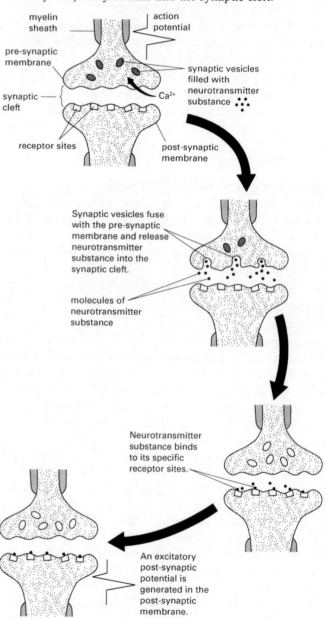

Transmission across an excitatory synapse

- The molecules of acetylcholine diffuse across the synaptic cleft trand bind to their specific receptors on the post-synaptic membrane.

- The binding of acetylcholine molecules to their receptors opens up sodium ion channels in the post-synaptic membrane, allowing the influx of sodium ions. Depolarization of the membrane occurs.

- The resting potential of the post-synaptic membrane is reversed and a new potential is generated.
- The new potential is called the **excitatory post-synaptic potential (EPSP)**.

On its own an EPSP normally does not produce sufficient depolarization to reach the threshold required to generate an action potential in the post-synaptic neurone. A number of EPSPs are required. EPSPs build up as more and more neurotransmitter substance binds to the receptors on the post-synaptic membrane. Threshold is reached when sufficient depolarization occurs in the post-synaptic membrane to generate an action potential in the neurone as a whole. The additive effect of EPSPs is called **temporal summation**.

So far the description of events refers to **excitatory synapses** but other synapses work in a different way. For example, **inhibitory synapses** respond to neurotransmitter not by promoting the inflow of sodium ions into the post-synaptic neurone and the depolarization of its post-synaptic membrane, but by promoting the outflow of potassium ions causing the polarization of the post-synaptic membrane to increase (**hyperpolarization**). Its threshold value is therefore greater, making the generation of an action potential in the post-synaptic neurone less likely. A post-synaptic neurone may be served by both types of synapse. Its activity is the result of the sum of their different inputs.

After synaptic transmission

If neurotransmitter were not removed from the synaptic cleft, its presence would stimulate the repeated generation of action potentials in the post-synaptic neurone and the continuous stimulation of the effector at the end of the chain of events.

If the effector is a muscle, it would be permanently contracted: a condition known as **tetanus**. Breaking down neurotransmitter substance prevents such an outcome.

- The enzyme **cholinesterase** located on the post-synaptic membrane catalyses the breakdown (hydrolysis) of acetylcholine into ethanoic (acetic) acid and choline.
- These products of hydrolysis pass back into the pre-synaptic knob.
- Neurotransmitter substance is re-synthesized in the pre-synaptic knob from the products and incorporated into synaptic vesicles.
- Calcium ions (Ca^{2+}) are actively transported out of the pre-synaptic knob, re-establishing their concentration gradient across the pre-synaptic membrane.

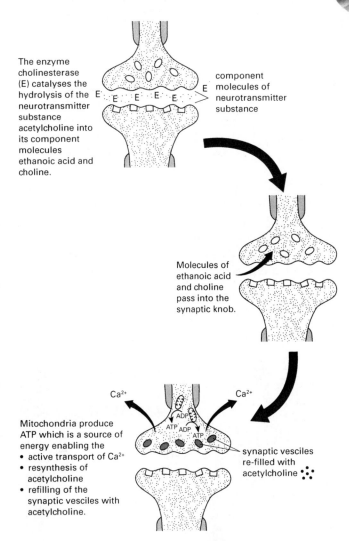

The enzyme cholinesterase (E) catalyses the hydrolysis of the neurotransmitter substance acetylcholine into its component molecules ethanoic acid and choline.

component molecules of neurotransmitter substance

Molecules of ethanoic acid and choline pass into the synaptic knob.

Mitochondria produce ATP which is a source of energy enabling the
- active transport of Ca^{2+}
- resynthesis of acetylcholine
- refilling of the synaptic vesicles with acetylcholine.

synaptic vesicles re-filled with acetylcholine

The hydrolysis, resynthesis, and repackaging of neurotransmitter substance

The effect of drugs on the synapse

Different drugs have their effect on the receptors of the post-synaptic membrane. Their action increases or reduces synaptic transmission.

- **Agonists** are drugs that mimic the structure of molecules of neurotransmitter substance and combine with and activate receptors. Their effect promotes the generation of action potentials. They act as stimulants.
- **Antagonists** are drugs which also mimic neurotransmitters but when they bind to receptors do not activate them. They block the generation of action potentials. They act as tranqillizers.

Fact file

The numerous mitochondria in the pre-synaptic knob generate the ATP required for the active transport of ions and refilling of synaptic vesicles with neurotransmitter substance. The presence of synaptic vesicles *only* in the synaptic knob and the location of receptors to which neurotransmitter substance binds *only* on the post-synaptic membrane means that synaptic transmission occurs *only* one way: pre-synaptic neurone → post-synaptic neurone.

Questions

1 Summarize the structure of a synapse.
2 What is an excitatory post-synaptic potential (EPSP)?
3 What is the difference between an excitatory synapse and an inhibitory synapse?

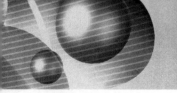

5.10 Muscles 1: structure

OBJECTIVES

By the end of the section you should

○ *know the gross structure and microscopic structure of skeletal muscle*

○ *be able to interpret the ultrastructure of a myofibril*

○ *know the structure of a neuromuscular junction*

○ *be able to explain the events across a neuromuscular junction*

Before you start it will help to read section **5.11** (sarcomeres).

When the muscles attached to the bones of the skeleton (skeletal muscle) contract (shorten) and relax (lengthen), the bones move. Looking at skeletal muscle tissue under the optical microscope shows a pattern of light and dark **striations** (bands) running from one side to another across fibre-like cells. Muscle tissue which shows a pattern of light and dark bands under the optical microscope is called **striated muscle**. Slender threads running the length of each muscle fibre are also visible. The threads are called **myofibrils**.

The electron microscope shows that

• each myofibril is made up of alternating light and dark bands

• the bands of myofibrils lying parallel next to one another line up – light to light, dark to dark – accounting for the striations running across each muscle fibre

• each myofibril consists of a number of longitudinal filaments – some thick, others thin

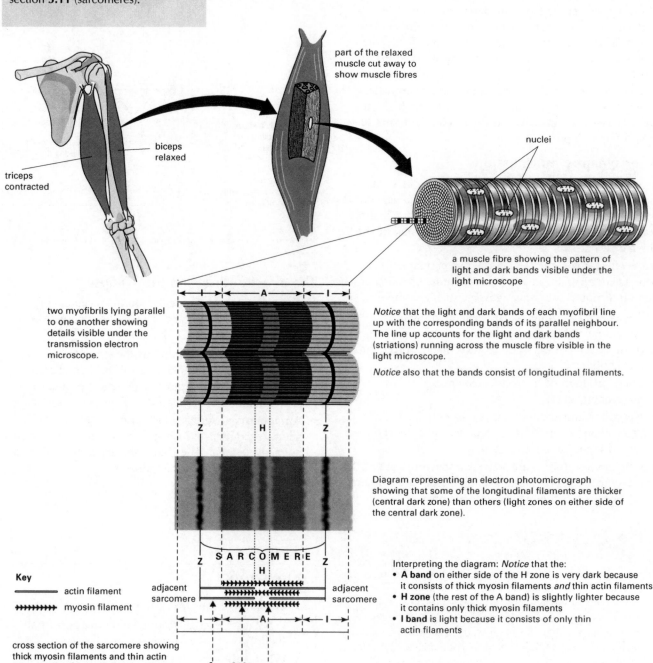

part of the relaxed muscle cut away to show muscle fibres

nuclei

biceps relaxed

triceps contracted

a muscle fibre showing the pattern of light and dark bands visible under the light microscope

two myofibrils lying parallel to one another showing details visible under the transmission electron microscope.

Notice that the light and dark bands of each myofibril line up with the corresponding bands of its parallel neighbour. The line up accounts for the light and dark bands (striations) running across the muscle fibre visible in the light microscope.

Notice also that the bands consist of longitudinal filaments.

Diagram representing an electron photomicrograph showing that some of the longitudinal filaments are thicker (central dark zone) than others (light zones on either side of the central dark zone).

Key

—————— actin filament

✛✛✛✛✛✛✛ myosin filament

adjacent sarcomere   adjacent sarcomere

Interpreting the diagram: *Notice* that the:
• **A band** on either side of the H zone is very dark because it consists of thick myosin filaments *and* thin actin filaments
• **H zone** (the rest of the A band) is slightly lighter because it contains only thick myosin filaments
• **I band** is light because it consists of only thin actin filaments

cross section of the sarcomere showing thick myosin filaments and thin actin filaments (end on) and their positional relationship with one another

Remember that

- thick filaments consist of the protein **myosin**
- thin filaments consist of the protein **actin**
- two other proteins called **tropomyosin** and **troponin** are bound to actin
- the enzyme **ATP-ase** is bound to myosin
- the arrangement of the filaments corresponds to the pattern of the light and dark bands of muscle tissue seen under the optical microscope

Notice that the thin actin filaments are anchored to a dark band called the **Z line** running through the middle of each light I band. The thick myosin filaments are anchored to the **M line** (not shown) running through the middle of the H zone. The region between one Z line and the next is called the **sarcomere**. It is the functional unit of muscle tissue.

Muscle fibres and the T-system

Remember that skeletal muscle tissue is made up of many fibre-like cells. Each fibre is:

- filled with cytoplasm (called **sarcoplasm**) containing many nuclei
- surrounded by the **sarcolemma** which is similar to the plasma membrane surrounding cells

… *except* that the sarcolemma folds inwards forming a series of transverse tubules which run through the sarcoplasm. The tubules are the components of the **T-system**.

The endoplasmic reticulum of a muscle fibre is called the **sarcoplasmic reticulum**. It forms swollen vesicles at the Z lines of the sarcomeres. Here the vesicles are in contact with the tubules of the T-system. The vesicles contain a high concentration of calcium ions (Ca^{2+}). The T-system and sarcoplasmic reticulum surround the myofibrils of the muscle fibre.

The diagram is a simplified representation of the arrangement. Refer to the diagram on page 68 to remind yourself of the details of the letter-labelled bands and lines.

Questions

1 What are myofibrils?
2 Draw a labelled diagram that identifies the pattern of light and dark bands of myofibrils.
3 What is a sarcomere?

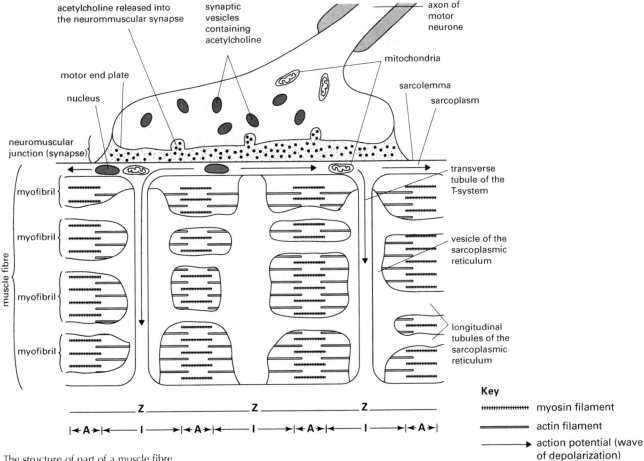

The structure of part of a muscle fibre

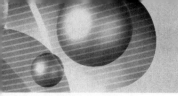

By the end of the section you should

○ *understand how a sarcomere contracts*

○ *be able to explain the roles of actin, myosin, calcium ions, and ATP in myofibril contraction*

○ *understand the properties of slow twitch and fast twitch skeletal muscle fibres*

Before you start it will help to read sections **4.07** (ATP) and **5.10** (sarcomere, neuromuscular junction, sarcolemma, T-system).

The **phase contrast microscope** alters the properties of light passing through it. This causes a difference in brightness in the cell's structures, improving contrast. The improvement makes it possible to see the structures one from another.

A myofibril consists of a chain of sarcomeres. Understanding how a sarcomere contracts is the key to understanding how a myofibril contracts and therefore the contraction of muscle tissue as a whole.

How science works (H)

How does muscle contract?

In the early 1950s, research groups at Cambridge University and University College London tackled the problem. Different types of microscopy provided the evidence.

- Electron microscopy showed that actin and myosin filaments remained the same length whether a sarcomere (and therefore a myofibril) was contracted or relaxed.

- Phase contrast microscopy showed that the pattern of light and dark bands changed during the contraction and relaxation of a muscle fibre.

Combined, the evidence strongly suggested that the filaments of actin and myosin slide past one another as the length of the sarcomere changes – long when relaxed; short when contracted. In 1954 both research groups proposed the sliding filament theory of muscle contraction to explain their observations.

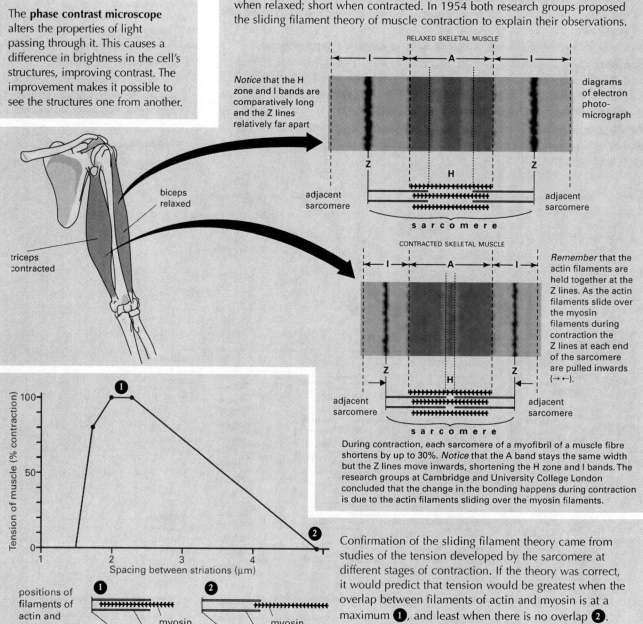

During contraction, each sarcomere of a myofibril of a muscle fibre shortens by up to 30%. *Notice* that the A band stays the same width but the Z lines move inwards, shortening the H zone and I bands. The research groups at Cambridge and University College London concluded that the change in the bonding happens during contraction is due to the actin filaments sliding over the myosin filaments.

Confirmation of the sliding filament theory came from studies of the tension developed by the sarcomere at different stages of contraction. If the theory was correct, it would predict that tension would be greatest when the overlap between filaments of actin and myosin is at a maximum ❶, and least when there is no overlap ❷. The results of experiments confirmed the prediction.

Contraction

How actin and myosin filaments slide past one another

Electron microscopy reveals cross bridges between filaments of actin and myosin. X-ray crystallography shows that the cross bridges move during contraction (*recall* X-ray crystallography from *AS level*)

When muscle is relaxed, the myosin heads are held away from the myosin binding sites on the actin filaments. When muscle is contracted, the myosin heads move out from their resting position and link to the myosin binding sites on the actin filaments, forming myosin/actin cross-bridges. The bridges stand at 45° from the myosin filaments when contraction begins.

Remember:

- Tropomyosin and troponin are proteins bound to actin. The diagram on page 72 shows the arrangement.
- Muscle tissue shows ATP-ase activity. The enzyme is located in each myosin head to which ADP and P_i are also bound when the muscle fibre is relaxed.
- Nerve impulses cause muscles to contract.

Contraction of muscle depends on the interactions between the T-system, sarcoplasmic reticulum, and actin, myosin and the proteins bound to them.

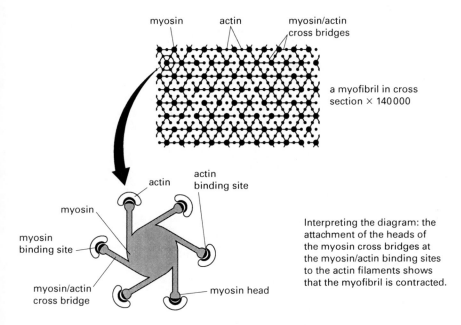

a myofibril in cross section × 140 000

Interpreting the diagram: the attachment of the heads of the myosin cross bridges at the myosin/actin binding sites to the actin filaments shows that the myofibril is contracted.

When a nerve impulse travelling along a motor neurone arrives at the **neuromuscular junction** (the synapse between the motor neurone and the sarcolemma of the muscle fibre) the **motor end plate** (a specialized part of sarcolemma) is depolarized.

- As a result a wave of depolarization travels along the sarcolemma and passes through the T-system into the muscle fibre.
- As a result the membranes of the vesicles of the sarcoplasmic reticulum become permeable to the calcium ions (Ca^{2+}) stored within them.
- As a result the calcium ions diffuse down their concentration gradient out of the vesicles and into the sarcoplasm surrounding the myofibrils.
- As a result the sites where myosin attaches to actin are uncovered and myosin/actin cross-bridges form, linking the filaments of actin and myosin.
- As a result the actin filaments are pulled over by the myosin towards the centre of the sarcomere.

With all the myofibrils of a sarcomere acting in this way, a force is generated which leads to a contraction (shortening) of the sarcomere (and therefore the myofibril, muscle fibre, and muscle tissue as a whole).

The diagram overleaf shows you the sequence of events.

Remind yourself to refer back to diagram on p.68 (5.10a muscle fibre structure).

Fact file

When muscle is relaxed the sites where myosin binds to actin are covered by tropomyosin. Calcium ions (Ca^{2+}) combining with troponin change its shape, causing it and tropomyosin to move away from the binding sites which are uncovered as a result.

Fact file

During strenuous exercise the rate of release of oxygen from haemoglobin is often not enough to keep up with the demand for generation of the ATP necessary to meet the energy requirements of muscle contraction. Muscles contain myoglobin (a protein similar to haemoglobin) which combines with oxygen, releasing it only when the supply of oxygen from haemoglobin falls off. They also store a substance called **creatine phosphate**. Its phosphate group can be transferred to ADP, producing ATP sufficient to help the muscles 'keep going' during strenuous exercise.

Myosin/actin cross-bridges project outwards from the myosin at regular intervals of 6–7 nm. Each bridge is separated by 60° from its neighbor and stands at 45° from the myosin when contraction begins.

Myosin moves actin during the contraction of muscle. The dashed line is a marker showing that contraction of a myofibril occurs as a result of the movement of actin filaments sliding over filaments of myosin. The overlap of actin and myosin filaments accounts for the changes in the pattern of light and dark bands of a sarcomere (and therefore a myofibril and a muscle fibre) described on page 70 during contraction of muscle from its relaxed state.

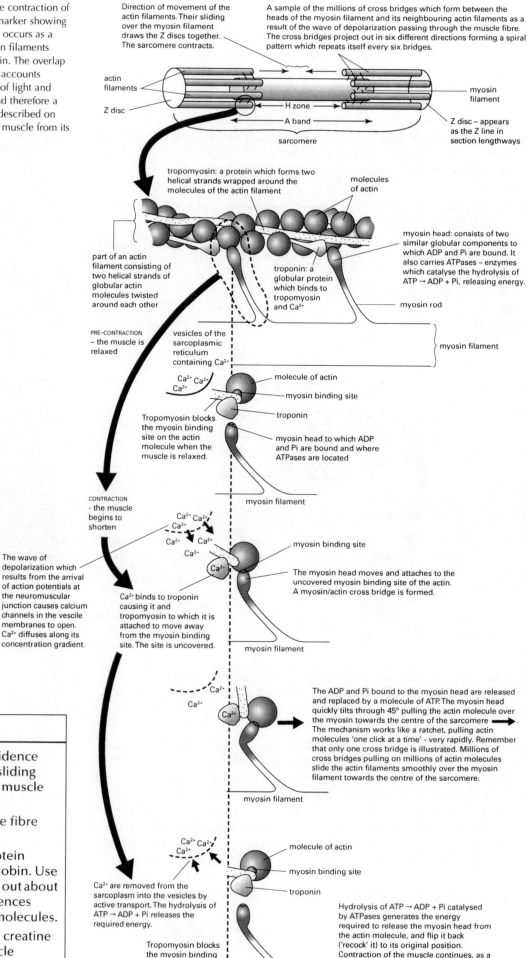

Direction of movement of the actin filaments. Their sliding over the myosin filament draws the Z discs together. The sarcomere contracts.

A sample of the millions of cross bridges which form between the heads of the myosin filament and its neighbouring actin filaments as a result of the wave of depolarization passing through the muscle fibre. The cross bridges project out in six different directions forming a spiral pattern which repeats itself every six bridges.

actin filaments

Z disc

myosin filament

H zone

A band

sarcomere

Z disc – appears as the Z line in section lengthways

tropomyosin: a protein which forms two helical strands wrapped around the molecules of the actin filament

molecules of actin

myosin head: consists of two similar globular components to which ADP and Pi are bound. It also carries ATPases – enzymes which catalyse the hydrolysis of ATP → ADP + Pi, releasing energy.

part of an actin filament consisting of two helical strands of globular actin molecules twisted around each other

troponin: a globular protein which binds to tropomyosin and Ca²⁺

myosin rod

myosin filament

PRE-CONTRACTION – the muscle is relaxed

vesicles of the sarcoplasmic reticulum containing Ca²⁺

Ca^{2+} Ca^{2+} Ca^{2+}

molecule of actin

myosin binding site

troponin

Tropomyosin blocks the myosin binding site on the actin molecule when the muscle is relaxed.

myosin head to which ADP and Pi are bound and where ATPases are located

myosin filament

CONTRACTION - the muscle begins to shorten

Ca^{2+} Ca^{2+} Ca^{2+} Ca^{2+} Ca^{2+} Ca^{2+}

myosin binding site

The myosin head moves and attaches to the uncovered myosin binding site of the actin. A myosin/actin cross bridge is formed.

The wave of depolarization which results from the arrival of action potentials at the neuromuscular junction causes calcium channels in the vescile membranes to open. Ca²⁺ diffuses along its concentration gradient.

Ca²⁺ binds to troponin causing it and tropomyosin to which it is attached to move away from the myosin binding site. The site is uncovered.

myosin filament

Ca^{2+} Ca^{2+}

The ADP and Pi bound to the myosin head are released and replaced by a molecule of ATP. The myosin head quickly tilts through 45° pulling the actin molecule over the myosin towards the centre of the sarcomere. The mechanism works like a ratchet, pulling actin molecules 'one click at a time' - very rapidly. Remember that only one cross bridge is illustrated. Millions of cross bridges pulling on millions of actin molecules slide the actin filaments smoothly over the myosin filament towards the centre of the sarcomere.

myosin filament

Questions

1 Summarize the evidence that supports the sliding filament theory of muscle contraction.

2 How does a muscle fibre contract?

3 Myoglobin is a protein similar to haemoglobin. Use the internet to find out about some of the differences between the two molecules.

4 What is the role of creatine phosphate in muscle contraction?

Ca^{2+} Ca^{2+} Ca^{2+}

Ca²⁺ are removed from the sarcoplasm into the vesicles by active transport. The hydrolysis of ATP → ADP + Pi releases the required energy.

Tropomyosin blocks the myosin binding site on the actin molecule. The muscle is relaxed.

molecule of actin

myosin binding site

troponin

Hydrolysis of ATP → ADP + Pi catalysed by ATPases generates the energy required to release the myosin head from the actin molecule, and flip it back ('recock' it) to its original position. Contraction of the muscle continues, as a result of the repeated cycle of forming and releasing myosin/actin cross bridges.

myosin filament

OBJECTIVES

By the end of the section you should

O *understand the properties of slow twitch and fast twitch skeletal muscle fibres*

Slow and fast skeletal muscle fibres

Vertebrate skeletal muscle consists of two types of muscle fibre: **slow twitch fibres** and **fast twitch fibres**. 'Twitch' refers to the contraction of a muscle fibre in response to the stimulus of a nerve impulse. Slow twitch and fast twitch is not the only difference between the types of fibres. Other differences are summarized in the table.

slow twitch	fast twitch
• red coloration is the result of a high content of myoglobin • respire aerobically • numerous mitochondria	• white coloration is the result of a low content of myoglobin • respire anaerobically • few mitochondria

Recall:

- Myoglobin is a pigment similar to haemoglobin. It absorbs oxygen.
- In mitochondria, the reactions of Krebs cycle and the electron transport chain produce large amounts of ATP.

In **slow twitch fibres**:

- Aerobic respiration enables slow twitch fibres to function for long periods without fatigue.
- However the rate of ATP production during aerobic respiration is relatively slow.

  As a result the contractions of slow twitch fibres are not very powerful.

In **fast twitch fibres**:

- Anaerobic respiration, which quickly produces ATP using stores of **creatine phosphate**, enables fast twitch fibres to function for short periods to maximum effect.

  As a result the contraction of fast twitch fibres are very powerful.

Recall however that anaerobic respiration in muscle fibres produces lactate. Fast twitch fibres therefore quickly fatigue as lactate accumulates even during short bursts of activity.

The proportions of slow twitch fibres and fast twitch fibres in muscle tissue is genetically determined. In most people the mix is about 50:50 but in trained athletes the proportions vary.

- Long distance runners and other endurance athletes tend to have more slow twitch fibres.
- Sprinters and other 'power' athletes tend to have more fast twitch fibres.

The proportions of slow twitch and fast twitch fibres making up our skeletal muscles may affect what sports we are naturally good at.

Fact file

The breakdown of creatine phosphate releases phosphate ions and energy. The phosphate ions may combine with ADP making ATP:

$$ADP + Pi \rightarrow ATP$$

Creatine phosphate is regenerated during aerobic respiration.

Questions

1 What are the differences between slow twitch and fast twitch muscle fibres?

5.13 Homeostasis

OBJECTIVES

By the end of the section you should

○ understand that homeostasis involves self regulating systems which maintain a constant internal environment

○ know that self regulation is the result of feedback mechanisms

○ be able to explain that homeostatic regulation enables organisms to function effectively (and therefore survive) in a wide range of environmental conditions

An organism's *external* environment is its habitat. Its *internal* environment is the tissue fluid which bathes the cells of its body, and the blood which circulates through its blood vessels.

Keeping conditions (external and internal) constant is called **homeostasis**. Internally, conditions kept constant include

- core body temperature
- blood pH (acidity/alkalinity)
- blood glucose concentration

Recall that the term metabolism refers to all of the chemical reactions taking place in cells. *Recall* also that optimum temperature and optimum pH refer to the respective values at which enzymes are most active and the rates of enzyme catalysed reactions are therefore at a maximum. Keeping core body temperature and blood pH constant at optimum values which maximize enzyme activity means that the metabolism of cells is at its most efficient. Keeping blood glucose concentration constant at a value which optimizes energy transfer within cells also contributes to the efficiency of cell metabolism.

Recall that the water potential of a solution is a measure of the concentration of water making up that solution. *Recall* also that blood plasma and tissue fluid are solutions of different solutes and that the movement of water (osmosis) between them depends on the difference in value between their respective water potentials. This difference accounts for the movement of water and substances in solution between cells, tissue fluid and blood. Glucose is an important solute in blood plasma and tissue fluid. Keeping blood glucose concentration constant contributes to the controlled movement of water and substances in solution between tissues and their blood supply.

By maximizing the efficiency of cell metabolism and keeping the composition of tissue fluid and blood constant (within narrow limits), cells function efficiently.

  ⊛ As a result the organism functions efficiently independent of changes (within wide limits) in its external environment.

  ⊛ As a result the organisms chances of survival are improved.

For example, mammals and birds have a range of homeostatic mechanisms which enable them to live in extreme environments: polar bears and penguins survive sub-zero polar conditions; camels the blistering heat of deserts.

Homeostasis is the result of self regulating systems which work by means of **feedback mechanisms**. Refer to the diagram as you read about the characteristics of self-regulating systems:

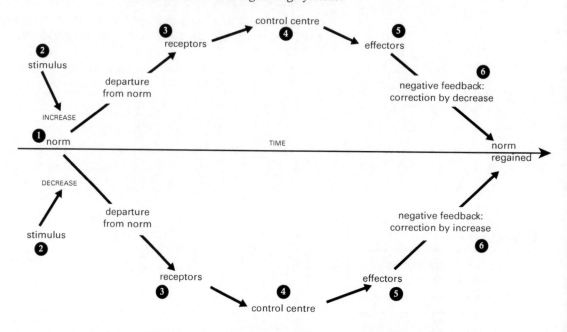

Characteristics of a self-regulating system

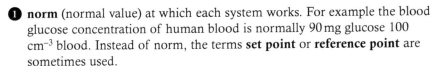

1 **norm** (normal value) at which each system works. For example the blood glucose concentration of human blood is normally 90 mg glucose 100 cm^{-3} blood. Instead of norm, the terms **set point** or **reference point** are sometimes used.

2 **stimuli** which cause deviations from the norm

3 **receptors** which detect deviations from the norm

4 **control centre** which receives information from receptors, coordinates the information, and sends instructions to effectors

5 **effectors** which bring about the responses needed to return the system to its norm

6 **feedback** which informs the receptors of the changes in the system caused by the effectors

Feedback **6** describes the situation where the information about changes in the system affects what happens to the changes in the future. When the information affects the system so that any change from the norm...

- reverses the direction of that change *towards* the norm, then we say that the feedback is **negative**
- causes more and more change *away* from the norm, then we say that the feedback is **positive**

Negative feedback maintains stability in a system. It controls the system so that conditions fluctuate around the norm. The system is self-adjusting. For example, human body temperature fluctuates and adjusts around a norm of 37°C. Homeostasis depends on the negative feedback mechanisms which enable systems to self-adjust.

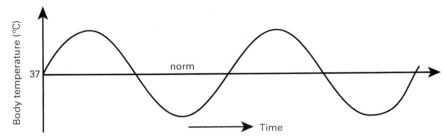

Positive feedback does *not* maintain stability in a system. It reinforces the original change and a chain reaction quickly develops. If positive feedback runs out of control then the system may destroy itself. In the real world, however, negative feedback of some sort eventually brings the self-reinforcing changes causing the chain reaction under control. For example, damaged tissues release substances that activate platelets in the blood. Activated platelets release substances which activate more platelets... and so on. A chain reaction quickly develops and a blood clot forms. This breaks the chain reaction and the norm is quickly re-established.

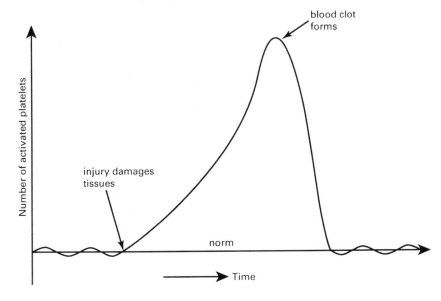

Fact file

Substances produced during certain bacterial infections temporarily shift the core body temperature above 37°C. The substances are called **pyrogens**. They affect the heat loss centre in the hypothalamus. The infected person appears flushed and produces a lot of sweat... both symptoms of a fever. If homeostatic control breaks down, then positive feedback reinforces further increase in core body temperature with possible fatal results.

Questions

1 What are the characteristics of self-regulating systems?

2 What is negative feedback?

3 Why does positive feedback not maintain stability in a system?

OBJECTIVES

By the end of the section you should

○ *be able to compare the contrasting mechanisms of temperature control in an ectothermic reptile and an endothermic mammal*

○ *know the mechanisms involved in heat production, conservation, and loss*

○ *understand how a constant body temperature is maintained in a mammal*

Before you start it will help to read sections **5.13** (characteristics of self-regulating systems).

The heat that warms animal bodies comes from the

• sun

• chemical reactions of metabolism

Ectotherms are animals which depend mainly on the sun as the source of body heat; **endotherms** depend mainly on their metabolism.

Birds and mammals are endotherms. High rates of metabolism release a lot of heat, which makes it possible to keep body temperature constant regardless of changes in the temperature of the environment. We call birds and mammals **homeotherms**.

The body temperature of other animals varies, often matching the temperature of the environment. We call them **poikilotherms**. The graph illustrates the point.

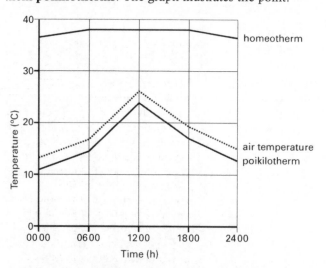

The body temperature of homeotherms and a poikilotherms and the air temperature recorded over 24 hours

Fact file

Not all parts of the body of a homeotherm are kept at a constant temperature, only the **body's core**. The body's surface where heat is exchanged with the environment is always cooler than the core temperature. The term **thermoregulatory** refers to the processes which enable an animal to maintain a constant core body temperature regardless of changes in the temperature of the environment.

Some poikilotherms achieve control of core body temperature despite rates of metabolism lower than homeotherms. Control is often achieved through different behaviours. For example, reptiles such as snakes and lizards sun themselves on rocks.

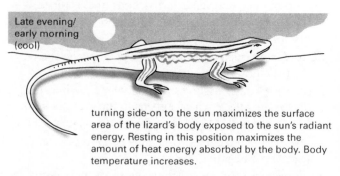

turning side-on to the sun maximizes the surface area of the lizard's body exposed to the sun's radiant energy. Resting in this position maximizes the amount of heat energy absorbed by the body. Body temperature increases.

turning head-on to the sun minimizes the surface area of the lizard's body exposed to the sun's radiant energy. Resting in this position minimizes the amount of heat energy absorbed by the body. Body temperature is stabilized.

How lizards achieve some control of core body temperature

Producing and losing body heat

The diagram represents the energy inputs and outputs of animals that live on land. The Sun's heat and the heat produced through the metabolism of cells are the components of inputs. Outputs are the ways body heat is lost to the environment. An animal is able to maintain a constant body temperature when the heat it gains (inputs) is equal to the heat it loses (outputs).

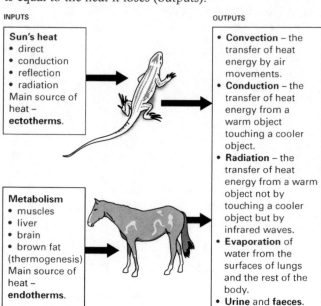

INPUTS

Sun's heat
• direct
• conduction
• reflection
• radiation
Main source of heat –
ectotherms.

Metabolism
• muscles
• liver
• brain
• brown fat (thermogenesis)
Main source of heat –
endotherms.

OUTPUTS

• **Convection** – the transfer of heat energy by air movements.
• **Conduction** – the transfer of heat energy from a warm object touching a cooler object.
• **Radiation** – the transfer of heat energy from a warm object not by touching a cooler object but by infrared waves.
• **Evaporation** of water from the surfaces of lungs and the rest of the body.
• **Urine** and **faeces**.

The faster the rate at which fats and sugars are oxidized in cells, the greater is the amount of heat energy released. Many of these oxidation reactions occur in cellular respiration and the rates of reaction are controlled by the hormone thyroxine produced and released by the thyroid gland. Cellular respiration is an important part of the cell's metabolism.

Thyroxine controls the metabolic rate of most endotherms at a level which enables them to maintain a constant core body temperature (usually 37°C in mammals; 41°C in birds). However, there is a cost: endotherms need much more food than ectotherms of equivalent size. For example, shrews (endotherms) eat food equivalent to their own body mass each day; cockroaches (ectotherms) can go without food for days. The extra food replaces the fats and sugars consumed in the metabolism which enables shrews to maintain a constant core body temperature.

Maintaining constant core body temperature

Remember that the temperature at the body's surface of an endotherm is cooler than the body's core.

The diagram summarizes the responses which enable endotherms (e.g. humans) to regulate their body temperature. The numbers ❸ to ❺ on the diagram and its checklist refer to the numbered characteristics of self-regulating systems listed on page 75.

In the lists:

- ❶ refers to the norm (normal value): in humans (and most mammals) the norm core body temperature is 37°C
- ❷ refers to the stimuli which cause deviations from the norm: here variations in the temperature of the environment cause changes in the temperature at the body's surface

Notice that the responses which regulate

- body surface (skin) temperature are voluntary responses
- core body temperature are involuntary responses

The homeostatic mechanisms controlling body surface temperature and core body temperature work together. Their interaction sets up voluntary and involuntary responses which compensate for changes in body surface temperature before any change in core temperature occurs.

Questions

1 Summarize the different ways body temperature is regulated in animals.

2 Explain the different ways an animal loses body heat to the environment.

3 How does the hormone thyroxine affect the release of heat by cells?

Checklist

Body surface temperature	Core body temperature
❸ Thermoreceptors in the...	
...*skin* detect changes in its temperature • heat receptors detect increases in temperature • cold receptors detect decreases in temperature	...*hypothalamus* of the brain detect changes in the temperature of the blood supplying the brain • heat loss centre is activated by increases in blood temperature • heat gain centre is activated by decreases in blood temperature
❹ The control centre in the...	
...*cortex* of the brain which enables us to think, feed and decide on our responses to stimuli (what we do). We say that the responses are voluntary.	...*hypothalamus* of the brain which not only detects changes in blood temperature but also sends signals via the autonomic nervous system controlling responses which do not require thinking and decision. We say that the responses are involuntary.
❺ The effectors which bring about the responses are...	
...the skeletal muscles which enable us to put our decisions into action ... putting on clothes or removing them depending on the skin temperature at which we feel comfortable	...the glands (sweat) and muscles (cause shivering, raise hairs, control blood flow) which enable the body to conserve or lose heat depending on its core temperature

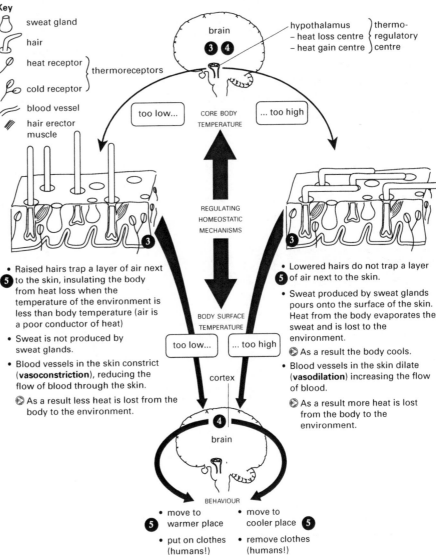

Key
- sweat gland
- hair
- heat receptor } thermoreceptors
- cold receptor
- blood vessel
- hair erector muscle

brain
❸ ❹

hypothalamus
– heat loss centre
– heat gain centre
} thermo-regulatory centre

too low... | CORE BODY TEMPERATURE | ... too high

REGULATING HOMEOSTATIC MECHANISMS

BODY SURFACE TEMPERATURE

too low... | ... too high

cortex

• Raised hairs trap a layer of air next ❺ to the skin, insulating the body from heat loss when the temperature of the environment is less than body temperature (air is a poor conductor of heat)
• Sweat is not produced by sweat glands.
• Blood vessels in the skin constrict (**vasoconstriction**), reducing the flow of blood through the skin.
  ▶ As a result less heat is lost from the body to the environment.

• Lowered hairs do not trap a layer ❺ of air next to the skin.
• Sweat produced by sweat glands pours onto the surface of the skin. Heat from the body evaporates the sweat and is lost to the environment.
  ▶ As a result the body cools.
• Blood vessels in the skin dilate (**vasodilation**) increasing the flow of blood.
  ▶ As a result more heat is lost from the body to the environment.

❹
brain

BEHAVIOUR
• ❺ move to warmer place
• put on clothes (humans!)

• move to cooler place ❺
• remove clothes (humans!)

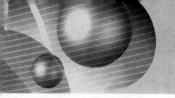

OBJECTIVES

By the end of the section you should

○ *know the factors that influence blood glucose concentration*

○ *understand the role of the liver in glycogenesis and gluconeogenesis*

○ *be able to explain the role of insulin and glucagon in controlling the uptake of glucose by cells*

○ *know the second messenger model of adrenaline and glucagon action*

○ *understand the difference between Type 1 and Type II diabetes and its control*

Before you start it will help to read section **5.05** (hormones).

Normally the concentration of glucose in the blood is about 90 mg glucose 100 cm⁻³ blood. However the value fluctuates according to circumstances.

- Following a meal the concentration of blood glucose increases as digested food is absorbed from the intestine into the bloodstream.

- During exercise the concentration of blood glucose decreases as glucose passes from the blood to vigorously contracting muscles, where it is used in cellular respiration.

Evening out fluctuations in blood glucose concentration is an example of homeostasis. The liver, muscles, and different hormones play an important role in the process.

Glucose in the body is stored as glycogen in liver and muscle. Different enzymes catalyse its

- synthesis: glucose → glycogen
- breakdown: glycogen → glucose

Different hormones control the activity of the enzymes.

Hormone	Target tissue	Source	Action
insulin	liver and muscle	pancreas	glucose → glycogen
glucagon	liver	pancreas	glycogen → glucose
adrenaline	muscle	adrenal glands	glycogen → glucose

Refer to the diagram on page 74 about the characteristics of self regulating systems.

The role of insulin and glucagon

The **pancreas** lies below the stomach in the first fold of the duodenum. It is an exocrine gland producing different digestive enzymes, which pass through the pancreatic duct to the duodenum. It is also an endocrine gland containing clusters of cells called the **islets of Langerhans**, which secrete hormones directly into the bloodstream.

Insulin is secreted by the numerous small **beta (ß) cells** of the islets in response to a *high* concentration of blood glucose (hyperglycaemia).

- Insulin makes the plasma membrane of liver cells and muscle cells more permeable to glucose.

  Ⓔ As a result more glucose is taken up from the blood by the cells.

- It activates **glycogen synthase** (and several other enzymes), which catalyses the condensation of glucose molecules forming glycogen in liver cells and muscle cells: glucose → glycogen.

The process is called **glycogenesis**.

- It promotes the conversion of glucose into lipids.

Overall, insulin *reduces* blood glucose concentration.

Glucagon is secreted by the less numerous, larger **alpha (α) cells** of the islets in response to a *low* concentration of blood glucose (hypoglycaemia).

- Glucagon reduces the permeability of the plasma membrane of liver cells to glucose.

  Ⓔ As a result less glucose is taken up from the blood by the cells.

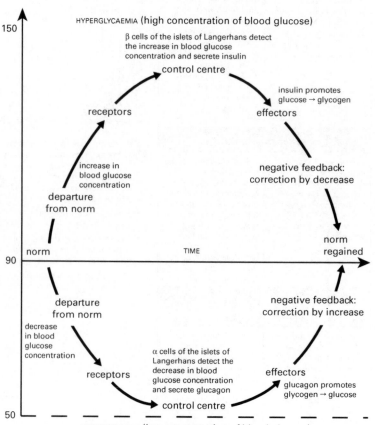

- It inhibits glycogen synthase (and other enzymes) catalysing the reactions of glycogenesis.
- It activates the enzyme **glycogen phosphorylase**, which catalyses the breakdown of glycogen in liver cells forming glucose: glycogen → glucose.

The process is called **glycogenolysis**.

- It activates **fructose bisphosphate phosphatase** (and other enzymes), which catalyses reactions that convert non-carbohydrate substances into glucose. The process is called **gluconeogenesis**.

Overall, glucagon *increases* blood glucose concentration.

Adrenaline secreted by the adrenal glands also affects the concentration of blood glucose. In response to a low concentration of blood glucose it

- *inactivates* glycogen synthase
- *activates* glycogen phosphorylase

☞ As a result blood glucose concentration *increases*.

Messengers and receptors

Remember:

- Hormones are **messenger molecules**. Insulin, glucagon, and adrenaline are examples.
- Receptors are proteins to which messenger molecules bind.

The different receptors which bind molecules of insulin, glucagon, and adrenaline are embedded in the phospholid bilayer of the plasma membrane of the cells of the hormones' target tissues.

$$insulin \xrightarrow{\text{target tissue}} liver \ and \ muscle$$

$$glucagon \xrightarrow{\text{target tissue}} liver$$

$$adrenaline \xrightarrow{\text{target tissue}} muscle$$

When insulin binds with its receptor

- endocytosis carries the hormone-receptor complex into the cytoplasm of the target cell
- the complex stimulates the golgi apparatus to bud off portions of material containing glucose carrier proteins
- the material passes to the cell surface where it fuses with the plasma membrane, increasing the number of glucose carrier proteins.

☞ As a result the uptake of glucose by the cell increases.

When glucagon and adrenaline combine with their respective receptors

- the enzyme **adenylate cyclase** is activated (adenylate cyclase is linked to the receptor protein)
- the enzyme catalyses the conversion of ATP to **cyclic (c)AMP**, which is an example of a **second** messenger molecule (hormone molecules are the **first** messenger)
- cAMP activates the enzyme glycogen phosphorylase.

☞ As a result the enzyme catalyses the breakdown
glycogen → glucose

☞ As a result glucose is released from the liver into the bloodstream.

☞ As a result blood glucose concentration increases.

Fact file

The activation of enzymes by cAMP is an example of a **reaction cascade**. This amplifies the response of target cells to hormones.

Diabetes

Without treatment, a person with **sugar diabetes** (a **diabetic**) may suffer from the different symptoms of hyperglycaemia.

- The pH of the blood falls, causing **acidosis**.
- The volume of water lost in the urine increases and is excessive.
- The blood supply to the body's extremities is reduced.

In the long term, **gangrene** may develop in fingers and toes deprived of the oxygen and nutrients carried in the blood.

There are two forms of diabetes:

- **Type 1 or insulin-dependent diabetes** (sometimes called **juvenile-onset diabetes**) where the pancreas does not produce enough insulin. The deficiency may be the result of
  o the individual's immune system destroying the β cells of the pancreas – an example of an auto-immune disease, or …
  o the gene encoding the synthesis of insulin is faulty – an example of a genetic disorder.

- **Type II or non-insulin-dependent diabetes** (sometimes called **late-onset diabetes**) where the pancreas produces enough insulin, at least to begin with, but the body's tissues become insensitive to it.

  ☞ As a result tissues cannot make use of blood glucose as a source of energy.

  ☞ As a result the β cells of the islets produce more insulin and the liver releases more glucose.

- Eventually the β cells become less able to produce enough insulin and tissues become more resistant to it.

  ☞ As a result the blood glucose concentration increases.

Treatment depends on the form of diabetes. Daily injections of insulin together with a healthy balanced diet regulate the blood glucose levels of individuals with Type I insulin-dependent diabetes. For those with Type II non-insulin-dependent diabetes successful control is often possible through a healthy balanced diet alone.

Questions

1 What is the difference between glycogenesis, glycogenolysis, and gluconeogenesis?

2 What happens when a molecule of insulin binds to its receptor protein embedded in the plasma membrane of a liver cell?

3 Why is cyclic (c) AMP called a secondary messenger molecule? What does cAMP do?

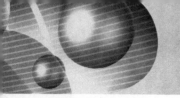

Fact file

At puberty each human ovary contains about 200 000 immature egg follicles.

The females of many mammal species advertize their fertility to males when they are ready to ovulate (the release of an egg, or eggs, from the ovary). For the female this is the time of **oestrous** (she is in 'heat') and the onset of her behaviour marks the beginning of the breeding season. The oestrous cycle describes the events during oestrous which lead to the production of eggs.

- Female sexual activity is restricted to the time of oestrous.

  Ⓔ As a result there is a good chance that eggs are fertilized.

- The lining of the uterus is reabsorbed at the end of the oestrous cycle.
- The oestrous cycle continues for an individual's lifetime.
- Bears, wolves, and other species which live in colder environments have only one period of oestrous a year – usually springtime.

  Ⓔ As a result the chances that offspring survive are improved with the coming of the warm season when more food is likely to be available.

- Cats, cows, and pigs have several periods of oestrous a year.

The human female usually produces one mature egg each month from the onset of puberty (age 11–14 years) to the beginning of **menopause** (age about 48 years). Then egg production becomes more and more irregular and stops altogether by the age of 52–55 years. The **menstrual cycle** describes the events which lead to the monthly production of a mature egg. The cycle is a type of oestrous cycle but with differences.

- Female sexual activity can occur at any phase in the menstrual cycle, not just during the time of oestrous.
- The lining of the uterus is not reabsorbed but breaks down at the end of each cycle. The surface tissue tears away and blood is released from broken blood vessels (**menstruation**). The tissue and blood pass through the vagina to the outside. This **menstrual flow** marks the onset of the **period** which lasts for several days. The uterus then returns to its resting state and a new menstrual cycle begins.
- The menstrual cycle does not continue for a lifetime. It lasts from the onset of puberty to the end of menopause.

Hormones control the menstrual cycle

The menstrual cycle occurs in chimpanzees and other primates. Here we focus on the human menstrual cycle.

The different phases of the human menstrual cycle take place over 28 days or so. During this time about 20 egg follicles in one of the ovaries begin to develop.

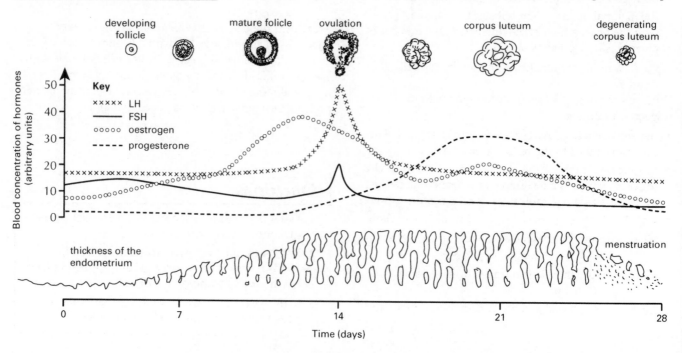

Development is under the control of hormones secreted by the pituitary gland and the ovary itself. The diagram on page 80 and its checklist of timings of each phase of the menstrual cycle are your guide to the coordination of events. *Remember* that the timings are average: they vary from person-to-person.

Checklist

Days 1–7	Days 8–14	Days 15–21	Days 22–28
Follicle Stimulating Hormone (FSH), secreted by the anterior pituitary gland into the blood stream, stimulates development of egg follicles in one of the ovaries. Most of them then break down but one continues to develop and begins to secrete the hormone **oestrogen**, which circulates in the blood and: • stimulates the growth of the **endometrium** (lining of the uterus) • inhibits the secretion of FSH from the pituitary gland • stimulates the secretion of luteinizing hormone (LH) from the pituitary gland	The developing follicle contains the maturing egg. • Secretion of more oestrogen stimulates the secretion of even more LH. • The hormone progesterone is secreted before ovulation (release of the egg from its follicle). • A surge of LH stimulates the mature follicle to rupture and release its egg (ovulation) on about day 14 of the cycle.	LH stimulates development of the empty ruptured follicle into the corpus luteum, which secretes progesterone that • stimulates further thickening of the endometrium • inhibits the secretion of FSH. As a result further ovulation is prevented. Overall the effect of progesterone is to prepare the body for pregnancy between days 14–21: the time that the egg is most likely to be fertilized.	If the egg is not fertilized, then the corpus luteum eventually breaks down. The level of progesterone in the blood falls and the endometrium begins to break down. The loss of tissue and blood through the vagina is called the menstrual flow and represents the time of menstruation (or the period). As the menstrual flow tapers off, the cycle restarts as the secretion of FSH increases once more.

Feedback

Feedback (negative and positive) regulates the menstrual cycle.

• The increasing level of oestrogen before ovulation results in *negative* feedback which reduces the secretion of FSH.

• Towards mid-cycle still higher levels of oestrogen plus pre-ovulatory progesterone result in *positive* feedback which stimulates the secretion of more LH.

    As a result the surge of LH stimulates ovulation.

The diagram summarizes events.

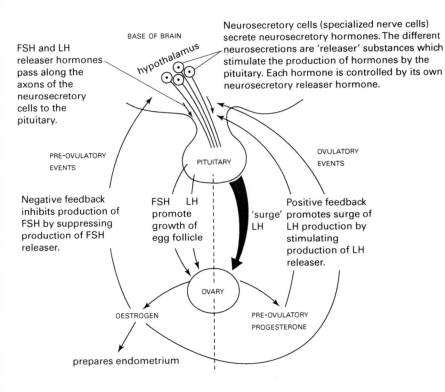

Questions

1 What is the difference between the oestrous cycle and the menstrual cycle?

2 Explain the feedback mechanisms that regulate the menstrual cycle

3 For animals that live in cold environments, what is the selective advantage of having one period of oestrous in spring?

5.17 The genetic code

You do not need to learn the names of genes, but some names show that scientists have a sense of humour! *Tinman* is an example. The gene is named after the character in the story of the Wizard of Oz who didn't have a heart. *Tinman* is one of the genes which regulates the development of heart tissue.

Recall that a **gene** is a section of **DNA** carrying information which enables a cell to combine amino acid units in the correct order forming a polymer (*or* part of a polymer) of peptide/polypeptide/protein. The information is carried in the sequence of bases on the nucleotides which make up the section of DNA forming a gene. The bases are adenine (A), thymine (T), cytosine (C), and guanine (G). The more amino acid units combined, the larger the polymer; peptide → polypeptide → protein. From now on *polypeptide* will include peptides/proteins.

Recall also that the **genetic code** is the sequence of bases of all of the genes of a cell and the information each gene carries. It works in the same way in the cells of all living things and is

- **a triplet code** – for each gene the information needed to assemble one amino acid unit in its correct place in a polypeptide molecule is contained in a sequence of three bases… the triplet is called a **codon**

- **non-overlapping** – the base of a triplet specifying the position of a particular amino acid unit does *not* contribute to specifying the positions of other amino acid units. So…

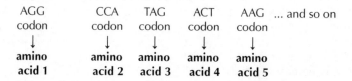

AGG	CCA	TAG	ACT	AAG	… and so on
codon	codon	codon	codon	codon	
↓	↓	↓	↓	↓	
amino acid 1	amino acid 2	amino acid 3	amino acid 4	amino acid 5	

Base A of this codon contributes to specifying the position of amino acid 1 in the polypeptide chain… …but does *not* contribute to specifying the position of the other amino acids 2–5 (likewise G, C, T)

- **degenerate** – the position of nearly all amino acids in a polypeptide molecule are specified by *more* than one codon.

Qs and As

Q How can a cell synthesize many more different polypeptides than there are genes which make up its genetic code?

A *Often, the synthesis of a polypeptide is the result of the combination of activity of two or more genes. The number of combinations is many more than the number of genes themselves.*

The nucleic acid family

Recall that a molecule of DNA is made up of two strands each consisting of many nucleotides joined together by condensation reactions. The strands coil round each other forming a **double helix** and are joined by hydrogen bonds between the bases **A T C** and **G**.

- A only bonds with T.
- G only bonds with C.

The arrangement is called **complementary base** pairing.

Recall also that the strands are **anti-parallel** to each other.

- One strand runs from carbon atom 3' of one nucleotide to carbon atom 5' of the next nucleotide in line… to carbon atom 3' of the next nucleotide… and so on.

- Its partner strand runs 5' → 3' → 5' … and so on in the opposite direction.

There are different types of RNA. The sequence of nucleotides (and therefore bases) of one of the strands of the section of DNA acts as a template (pattern) against which RNA is synthesized. For example …

Messenger RNA (mRNA) is synthesized in the cell nucleus. Its molecules are each usually single stranded, each strand consisting of many nucleotides joined together by condensation reactions. The sequence of nucleotides (and therefore bases) forming a strand of RNA is a *complement* of the sequence of nucleotides (and therefore bases) of the strand of the section of DNA which is the template against which the RNA strand forms.

Transfer RNAs (tRNA) tRNAs are smaller molecules than mRNA. The diagram represents the shape of a molecule of tRNA in the form of a cloverleaf. The shape is held by the hydrogen bonding of complementary bases within the molecule.

- Notice in the diagram that an amino acid is attached at one end of the molecule which ends in a sequence of CCA. The sequence forms the **amino acid accepting site**. Transfer RNAs act as carriers of amino acids during polypeptide synthesis. Each type of amino acid is carried by its own type of tRNA.

- *Remember* that there are at least 20 different amino acids. There are, therefore, at least 20 different types of tRNA.

- Notice also the three bases which form the part of the molecule of tRNA labelled the anticodon. These bases are complementary to the mRNA codon encoding the amino acid it carries. There are as many different arrangements of the sequence of the anticodon as there are amino acids.

Ribosomal RNA (rRNA) combines with protein forming ribosomes. Each ribosome is a site where mRNA and tRNA interact, synthesizing polypeptides.

Comparing nucleic acids

Comparing nucleic acids highlights their similarities: each is a molecule of polynucleotide formed from many nucleotide units joined together by condensation reactions. Each nucleotide carries a base. However there are differences. The table summarizes the structure, make up, and function of nucleic acids.

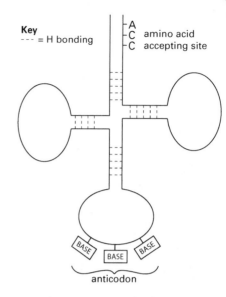

Key
--- = H bonding
A
C amino acid
C accepting site

anticodon

A transfer RNA (tRNA) molecule

Questions

1 What does it mean when we say that the genetic code is non-overlapping?

2 What is a code? Use the internet to help you answer the question.

3 Explain the role of each type of RNA.

Nucleic acids compared. Note that the base uracil (U) substitutes for thymine in mRNA and tRNA.

	DNA	mRNA	tRNA
Polynucleotide strand	double	single	single
Origin	replicated by parent DNA	transcribed against DNA template	transcribed against DNA template
Number of bases	variable: many thousands	variable: many hundreds to a few thousands	75–90
Pentose sugar	deoxyribose	ribose	ribose
Bases	ATCG	AUCG	AUCG
Ratio of bases	A:T = 1 C:G = 1	variable	variable
Shape of molecule	double helix	usually a single strand which can twist into a variety of shapes	single strand in the form of a 'clover leaf'
Location	mainly in the nucleus	made in the nucleus; found in the cytoplasm	made in the nucleus; found in the cytoplasm
Function	carries genetic information inherited from parent DNA	carries genetic information from the nucleus to the ribosomes where polypeptides are synthesized	binds to amino acids and carries them to the mRNA combined with ribosomes

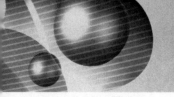

5.18 Polypeptide synthesis

Polypeptide synthesis is a two stage process.

- **Transcription** – the synthesis of mRNA from the DNA template of a gene. The information carried in the sequence of bases of the gene is copied in the sequence of bases of the mRNA transcribed.

- **Translation** – the conversion of the information in mRNA to make a polypeptide. The information is carried in the sequence of bases of the mRNA (itself a complementary copy of the base sequence of the gene against which the mRNA was transcribed) and determines (decides) the sequence (order) in which amino acids join together forming a polypeptide.

The diagram and its checklist are your guide to the sequence of events.

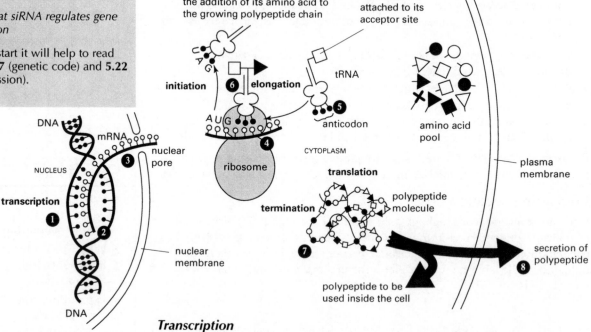

Transcription

❶ • The enzyme **DNA helicase** catalyses the breaking of the hydrogen bonds that link the base pairs of a double-stranded section of DNA carrying the gene to be transcribed. The DNA unzips and its strands separate. The bases of each strand are exposed.

- Some base sequences of one of the unzipped strands (the transcribing strand) carry the genetic information which encodes polypeptide synthesis. Its unzipped partner strand does not carry genetic information.

- Each sequence of bases of the transcribing strand which encodes the synthesis of polypeptide is called an **exon**.

- The sequences of bases that do *not* encode for polypeptide are called **introns**. Sometimes introns are called 'silent' or 'junk' DNA (bacterial DNA does not contain introns).

❷ • mRNA is synthesized on the transcribing DNA strand. The enzyme **RNA polymerase** first binds to a **promoter** sequence on the transcribing strand, initiating transcription. The enzyme then moves along the transcribing strand, adding RNA nucleotides to the growing mRNA strand. The bases of the nucleotides are complementary to the exposed bases of the transcribing strand.

- A **cap** of G (guanine) is added to the 5′ end, and a **poly-A tail** (150–200 adenines) to the 3′ end of the pre-mRNA molecule.

- The growing mRNA strand lengthens in the 5′ → 3′ direction.

- A strand of **pre-mRNA** (precursor mRNA) is produced. Pre-mRNA carries exons and introns which are complements of the exons and introns of the transcribing strand.

- In eukaryotic cells, further processing occurs which adds signalling sequences to and removes introns from the pre-mRNA. The process is called **editing**. Enzymes called **spliceosomes** catalyse the joining together of the exons. The result is a strand of **mature mRNA**.

3 • Strands of mature mRNA pass from the nucleus through the nuclear pores of the nuclear membrane into the cytoplasm of the cell. Its poly-A tail facilitates (makes easy) the passage of each strand.

Translation

4 • A strand of mature mRNA binds to a ribosome. Binding is facilitated by its poly A-tail. Its 5′ cap signals the point of attachment. The ribosome moves along the strand until it reaches an **initiation codon**. This is usually AUG and signals the beginning of a gene.

5 • Molecules of tRNA collect amino acids from the 'pool' of amino acids dissolved in the cytoplasm of the cell. *Remember* that each type of amino acid is carried by its own type of tRNA. The combination of an amino acid with its particular tRNA requires energy released by the hydrolysis of ATP. The process is called **activation**. The tRNA/amino acid combinations move towards a ribosome.

6 • The tRNA/amino acid combination which carries the anticodon UAC combines with its complement, the first codon AUG. This is initiation and translation begins. The second codon of the mRNA then attracts its complementary tRNA anticodon in a second tRNA/amino acid combination. The ribosome holds the two combinations in place while a peptide bond forms between the two amino acids. The reaction is catalysed by the enzyme **peptidyl transferase**.

- Once the peptide bond forms, the bond between the first (initiation) molecule of tRNA and its amino acid is hydrolysed and the unbound tRNA is released from its complementary mRNA codon. The third codon of the mRNA attracts its complementary tRNA anticodon, in a third tRNA/amino acid combination. The ribosome moves along to hold it in place while a peptide bond forms between the amino acid which its tRNA carries and the second amino acid. The bond between the second molecule of tRNA and its amino acid is hydrolysed and the unbound tRNA is released from its complementary mRNA codon.

  - As a result a strand of polypeptide forms, one amino acid at a time, according to the particular sequence of the codons of the mRNA coding tRNA/amino acids combinations to assemble in a particular order. The process is called **elongation**.

7 • The ribosome moves along the length of mRNA until it reaches a **stop codon** UAA, UGA, or UAG. This codon does not attract an anticodon but encodes a **releasing factor**. The bond between the terminal (end) tRNA molecule and its amino acid is hydrolysed and the completed polypeptide molecule released. The process is called **termination**.

- Polypeptide chains may then fold to form secondary and tertiary structures. Several chains may combine to form a quaternary structure.

- Polypeptides used inside cells are usually made on free ribosomes and released into the cytoplasm.

8 • Polypeptides to be exported from cells are usually made on the ribosomes of the endoplasmic reticulum and transported to the Golgi apparatus. Here they are modified and packaged into vesicles which bud off from the Golgi. The vesicles pass to the plasma membrane from which they are secreted by exocytosis or where they form membrane proteins.

Questions
1 Explain the difference between an exon and an intron.
2 Briefly summarize the processes of transcription and translation.
3 What is a polysome?

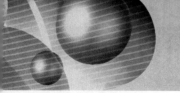

5.19 Gene mutation

OBJECTIVES

By the end of the section you should

○ *know that mutation might result in a different sequence of amino acid units in the encoded polypeptide… but not always*

○ *know that mutated proto-oncogenes are called oncogenes*

○ *understand that oncogenes and mutated tumour suppressor genes allow the rate of cell division to increase*

○ *know that the chain-termination method is one way of sequencing the bases of DNA*

Recall that the term **mutation** refers to a change in the arrangement or the amount of genetic material in a cell. The change may affect just one gene or a chromosome or part of a chromosome carrying many genes. Mutations in sex cells (sperms or eggs) are **inherited**; we say that the mutations are **hereditary**. Mutations in other (body) cells are *not*; we say that the mutations are **acquired**.

Gene mutations are the result of copying errors in the sequence of bases of their DNA. They occur during DNA replication. If only one base is involved, then the copying error is called a **point mutation**. There are two types:

• base pair **deletions** (bases are lost) or **insertions** (bases are added)

• base pair **substitutions** (bases are replaced with others)

Deletions or insertions alter the sequence of the bases downstream of the **locus** (position of a gene on a chromosome) on the DNA strands where the mutation takes place. *Recall* that during transcription the sequence of the bases of the DNA of a gene is copied in the sequence of bases of the mRNA transcribed; and that during translation the base sequence of the transcribed mRNA determines the order in which amino acid units join up forming a polypeptide. *Recall* also that the information needed to assemble one amino acid unit in its correct place in a polypeptide is contained in the sequence of bases called a codon.

The diagram illustrates the point. *Notice:*

• The codons are set out for mRNA (U instead of T) and are therefore complements of the DNA codons from which the mRNA is transcribed. The accepted abbreviations of the amino acid encoded by the codons are included.

• The sequence of amino acids downstream of the point mutation causing either deletion or insertion is changed compared with the normal sequence encoded by the non-mutated gene. We say that the mutation causes a **frame-shift**, and frame shift mutations can significantly affect the structure and therefore function of polypeptides.

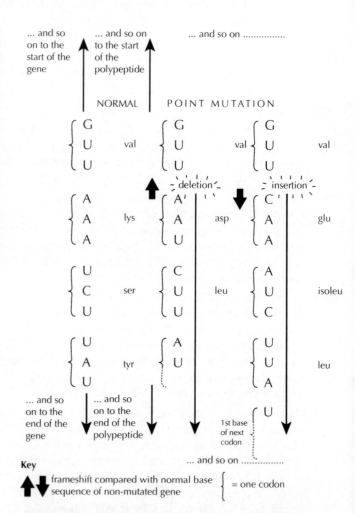

You do not need to remember the base sequence of codons or the amino acid each codon specifies. However you may need to interpret them (or similar) in an exam.

Qs and As

Q Why may frame-shift mutations affect the structure and therefore function of polypeptides?

A *The function of polypeptides depends on their structure and therefore shape. Their shape is determined by hydrogen bonding and the interactions between the different R groups of the amino acids making up the polypeptide in question. The change in the sequence of R groups of the amino acid units downstream of the point mutation changes the interactions between them and the shape of the polypeptide molecule. The changed shape affects the function of the polypeptide.*

Substitutions also alter the sequence of bases within a codon, but not downstream of the mutation. The alteration may change the amino acid unit at the point of the mutation… or *not*. *Remember* that the genetic code is **degenerate**. All amino acids but two are encoded by more than one codon – in the case of the amino acid leucine there are six alternatives! This means that if the substitution replaces a base within a codon with a base of an alternative codon encoding the same amino acid, then the amino acid sequence of the polypeptide as a whole will not change, even though the base sequence of the codon has. This sort of mutation is called a **silent** mutation.

Causes of mutations

Gene mutations occur spontaneously as random events during DNA replication. However various factors in the environment increase the mutation rate. An environmental factor that causes mutation is called a **mutagen**. Ionizing radiation (e.g. X-rays, gamma rays) and different chemicals are mutagens.

- Ionizing radiation damages DNA by stripping electrons from the atoms of its molecules (ionizes the atoms).
- Alkylating agents are chemicals which transfer $-CH_3$ (methyl) and $-CH_3CH_2$ (ethyl) groups to DNA molecules, altering their activity.

Genes and cell division

Mutagens often cause mutations in the genes which control the rate of cell division. Normally cell division stops when the particular task requiring more cells is complete – a cut is healed, for example. However if mutagens cause mutations in the genes controlling cell division, then the cells proliferate and cell division runs out of control. A mass of cells called a **tumour** develops.

If the cells of a tumour do not spread from the point of origin then the tumour is said to be **benign**. If they break away from the tumour and spread elsewhere in the body (**metastasis**) then the tumour is said to be **malignant**. The word **cancer** refers to malignant tumours. Mutagens which cause cancer are called **carcinogens**.

They cause mutations in:

- **proto-oncogenes** which encode proteins that stimulate normal cell division. Mutated proto-oncogenes are called **oncogenes**. Their activity results in
  o increased production of the proteins stimulating cell division or …
  o an increase in the activity of the proteins themselves
  As a result cell division is over-stimulated and cells proliferate. A tumour develops.
- **tumour suppressor genes** which encode proteins that
  o inhibit cell division
  o attach cells to one another and anchor them in their proper place
  o repair damaged DNA before it can be replicated.

Mutation of tumour-suppressor genes inactivates them.
  As a result cell division continues when it should stop and cells proliferate. A tumour develops.

If the tumours caused because of the activity of oncogenes or mutated tumour suppressor genes undergo metastasis, then cancers develop.

DNA sequencing

Knowing the sequence of the human genome and advances in DNA technology enable us to identify and locate genes – particularly those that affect our risk of developing different diseases, and mutant genes which are the cause of genetic disorders.

The **chain-termination method** is one way of sequencing the bases of DNA. The diagram and its checklist are your guide to the technique.

Checklist

❶ The DNA of entire chromosomes is fragmented using specific restriction enzymes.

❷ The fragments are cloned using PCR.

❸ Each fragment is sequenced.

❹ The sequences are assembled into an overall sequence of the DNA of each chromosome.

Whole genomes, including the human genome, have been sequenced using the chain termination method. The technology is highly automated and combined with sophisticated computer software. This makes it possible to assemble sequences of DNA fragments into a whole genome.

Questions

1 What is a point mutation?

2 Explain why a mutation may be silent.

3 Why do oncogenes and mutations in tumour suppressor genes increase the risk of cancer?

4 The chain-termination method is one way of sequencing the bases of DNA. Summarize the method.

5.20 Gene expression: totipotent cells and differentiation

OBJECTIVES

By the end of the section you should

O *know that totipotent cells can mature into any body cell*

O *understand that only part of the DNA of totipotent cells is expressed*

O *know that tissue culture makes it possible to produce clones of plants which retain the favourable characteristics of the parent plant*

Before you start it will help to read sections **5.18** (polypeptide synthesis) and **5.26** (*in vitro*).

Recall that gene expression refers to the events of transcription and translation which result in the synthesis of polypeptide.

The adult of a sexually reproducing organism develops from a **zygote** (a fertilized egg). During development successive cycles of cell division by mitosis form the tissues and organs of the adult body.

How is it possible that all of the different types of cell that form tissues and organs arise from a single cell (the zygote)?

Cells that give rise to *all* of the cell types of an organism are said to be **totipotent**. In mammals, only the zygote and the small cluster of cells which arise from the first few cycles of mitosis following fertilization are totipotent. Further mitotic cycles produce a hollow ball of cells containing a mass of cells within. These cells are descendants of the totipotent cells but different from them. They can produce *most* but not all of the cells of an organism. We say that the cells are **pleuripotent**.

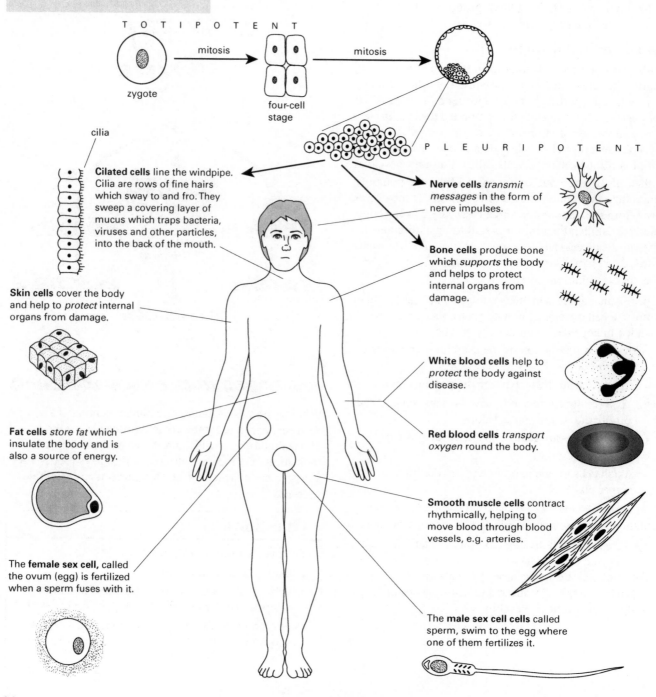

T O T I P O T E N T

zygote → mitosis → four-cell stage → mitosis →

P L E U R I P O T E N T

cilia

Cilated cells line the windpipe. Cilia are rows of fine hairs which sway to and fro. They sweep a covering layer of mucus which traps bacteria, viruses and other particles, into the back of the mouth.

Skin cells cover the body and help to *protect* internal organs from damage.

Fat cells *store fat* which insulate the body and is also a source of energy.

The **female sex cell,** called the ovum (egg) is fertilized when a sperm fuses with it.

Nerve cells *transmit messages* in the form of nerve impulses.

Bone cells produce bone which *supports* the body and helps to protect internal organs from damage.

White blood cells help to *protect* the body against disease.

Red blood cells *transport oxygen* round the body.

Smooth muscle cells contract rhythmically, helping to move blood through blood vessels, e.g. arteries.

The **male sex cell cells** called sperm, swim to the egg where one of them fertilizes it.

During development the differences between cells occurs because only some of the genes of the pleuripotent cells which give rise to them are expressed, and then expressed in different ways. Differences in gene expression (and therefore translation) result in the synthesis of different polypeptides which determine what types of cell pleuripotent cells become. The process is called **differentiation**. More than 200 different types of cell make up the human body. Each type is **specialized** in ways that enable that type to carry out a particular function: for example, neurones transmit nerve impulses, muscle cells contract.

The pattern of gene expression determines the differentiation of cells and their pattern of development. It ensures that tissues and organs develop in the right place at the right time in the embryo. Getting place and time right depends on switching the transcription and translation of genes on and off in the correct order.

In plants, totipotent cells are part of the tissues at the tip of the shoot and roots. The tissues are called **apical meristems**. Unlike the totipotent cells of animals, the cells remain totipotent and are active throughout the life of the plant. This means that plants continue to grow over many years, developing new tissues and organs.

Tissue culture

Differentiated plant cells can revert to totipotency if grown *in vitro* in the correct conditions. The process is called **dedifferentiation**. It shows that in plants, differentiation does not necessarily mean that the pattern of gene expression which switches genes on and off is irreversible. Dedifferentiation occurs naturally in animals like worms and amphibians but can only be achieved in mammals *in vitro*, and even then the technique is difficult.

The technique of **tissue culture** (micropropagation) makes use of the totipotency of meristems and the ability of differentiated plants cells to revert to a totipotent state. Growing **explants** (the part of the plant to be cultured) *in vitro* in tissue culture enables us to grow thousands of genetically identical plants (**clones**) from a single parent plant.

- Explants are placed in growth medium (a liquid or gel) that contains all the ingredients that the pieces of tissues need to grow.
- Conditions are sterile.
  - As a result, the new plants are free of disease.
- Temperature is optimized, encouraging growth.

The advantages of producing clones of plants by tissue culture are that the plants are

- healthy
- genetically identical to each other (clones) and to the parent plant.
  - As a result all of the desirable qualities of the parent plant (e.g. flower colour, fruit quality, resistance to disease) are retained in the clone.

Successfully growing explants in tissue culture into healthy plants depends on the

- *growth medium* – different mixtures of plant growth substances, salts and other nutrients are used, depending on the plant species and the product wanted: for example, the growth medium used to produce embryoid bodies for 'artificial seeds' is different from the medium used to produce whole plantlets
- *culture environment* – explants grow only if pH and light conditions are suitable for the plant species in question
- *growing conditions* – plantlets are more delicate than seedlings. Some form of protection (plastic sheeting, greenhouse) helps them to survive the early stages of growth following planting out into trays filled with a suitable artificial soil mix. After several weeks the plantlets are more hardy and able to survive in the open.

Questions

1. What is a zygote? Why is a zygote said to be totipotent?
2. Summarize the conditions needed to grow successfully pieces of plant (explants) in tissue culture.
3. Explain the process of dedifferentiation of cells.

5.21 Stem cells

OBJECTIVES

By the end of the section you should

○ *know what stem cells are*

○ *understand the potential of stem cell therapy*

○ *be able to evaluate the use of stem cell therapy in treating different human disorders*

Before you start it will help to read sections **5.20** (potency of cells) and **5.26** (*in vitro*).

Recall that totipotent cells can give rise to *all* cell types of an organism; their descendants are pleuripotent cells which can produce *most* but not all cell types.

Recall that a zygote is totipotent. It divides by mitosis, producing totipotent daughter cells. Further divisions give rise to an embryo consisting of a hollow ball of cells containing a mass of cells within. These cells are pleuripotent. As development of the embryo continues multipotent cells develop. The sequence runs like this:

development of the embryo →

	totipotent cells	→	pleuripotent cells	→	multipotent cells
potential to differentiate into different cell types	all		most		limited

Stem cells are defined by their

• potential to differentiate into different cell types

• ability to divide continually by mitosis, producing new generations of cells.

Two types of division are possible:

• **symmetric division** which results in identical daughter stem cells

• **asymmetric division** which results in different daughter cells. One gives rise to stem cells, the other differentiated cells.

The types of cell, and number of types differentiated, depend on the source of stem cell. Totipotent and pleuripotent cells have the potential to differentiate into many more types of cell than multipotent cells.

• **Embryonic stem cells** derive from totipotent and pleuripotent cells.

• **Adult stem cells** usually derive from multipotent cells.

The science behind stem cell therapy

In adult humans some stem cells remain in the body. For example, adult stem cells in the marrow of the leg bones and arm bones give rise to different types of blood cell. It seems likely that small numbers of stem cells remain in other body tissues as well. If injury or disease damages a tissue, then its stem cells divide and differentiate into new cells, repairing the damage. Stimulating embryonic or adult stem cells to multiply and differentiate *in vitro* has the potential of making unlimited supplies of different types of cell available to be transplanted into people whose tissues are so damaged as to be beyond self-repair. This is called **stem cell therapy**.

The potential of stem cell therapy

Remember that embryonic stem cells can differentiate into many types of cell other than adult stem cells. This makes them ideal for different stem cell therapies. However their use is controversial because the current methods of obtaining embryonic stem cells destroys the embryos from which the cells are sourced.

Using adult stem cells to repair damaged tissue is less controversial because embryos are not destroyed. Also, sourcing the cells from the person who is to receive treatment removes the risk of rejection when the cells are transplanted back into the person.

Putting right genetic disorders using stem cell therapy is another possibility. **Cystic fibrosis (CF)** is a genetic disorder. Mutation of the CFTR gene disrupts the movement of chloride ions out of the epithelial cells lining the airways. The normal gene encodes the polypeptide which forms chloride ion channels in the plasma membrane of the cells. People in whom the mutant gene is expressed produce too much mucus, clogging their airways.

Fact file

Recently adult stem cells have been manipulated *in vitro* to produce embryonic-like stem cells. The adult cells are dedifferentiated. Since embryos are not the source of these stem cells, the technique may help to make embryonic stem cell therapy more acceptable.

One possible form of treatment for cystic fibrosis using stem cells runs like this:

```
┌─────────────────────────────────────┐
│ bone marrow stem cells taken from CF │
│ individuals are genetically modified,│
│ replacing the faulty CFTR gene with  │
│ a normal one.                        │
└─────────────────────────────────────┘
                   │
                   ▼
┌─────────────────────────────────────┐
│ The genetically modified stem cells  │
│ are stimulated to differentiate into │
│ airway epithelial cells.             │
└─────────────────────────────────────┘
                   │
                   ▼
┌─────────────────────────────────────┐
│ The differentiated genetically       │
│ modified airway epithelial cells are │
│ transplanted back into the person    │
│ they came from.                      │
└─────────────────────────────────────┘
                   │
                   ▼
┌─────────────────────────────────────┐
│ The normal CFTR gene is expressed    │
│ and the airway epithelial cells work │
│ properly.                            │
└─────────────────────────────────────┘
                   │
                   ▼
┌─────────────────────────────────────┐
│ The transplanted cells are not       │
│ rejected by the person's body because│
│ they are genetically identical and   │
│ immunologically compatible with it.  │
└─────────────────────────────────────┘
```

Evaluating stem cell therapy

Currently, in the UK, stem cells taken from the bone marrow and from the blood of the umbilical cord are used to treat people suffering from different types of cancer. Anti-cancer drugs destroy not only cancer cells but also the stem cells that give rise to blood cells. Transplanting healthy bone marrow cells into the cancer patient aims to reverse this side-effect.

Potentially, stem cell therapy could be used to treat a wide range of human disorders. However many difficulties remain.

- Stem cell lines (cultures of stem cells) which reliably produce the desired cell types must be available.
- Treatments should work well for the life-time of the person receiving the stem cells.
- Stem cells must not trigger side effects in the person receiving them. For example, there are concerns that stem cells might trigger adverse immune responses or development of cancers.

In Europe, North America, and Australasia different clinical trials of stem cell therapy are providing encouraging results. In China stem cells are routinely used to treat a range of disorders. There, research has not been so affected by the ethical issues which have caused vigorous debate in other developed countries.

Fact file

In January 2009 President Barack Obama lifted the restrictions of US government funding of stem cell research imposed by the previous administration.

Questions

1 Explain the difference between totipotent cells, pleuripotent cells, and multipotent cells.

2 Summarize the difficulties of using stem cell therapy in the treatment of disease.

3 Why is therapy using embryonic stem cells controversial?

5.22 Gene expression and its regulation

In bacteria groups of genes encoding proteins with related functions are arranged in units called **operons**. The operon model of gene expression was developed in 1961 by the French biologists Francois Jacob and Jacques Monod. Understanding how the **operon model** works will help you to understand how gene expression is regulated.

An operon is a length of bacterial DNA consisting of the

* **operator** which binds a protein called **repressor**
* **promoter** which binds RNA polymerase
* **structural** genes which transcribe mRNA

Another gene called the **regulator** is not part of the operon and is usually upstream of it. The regulator gene encodes repressor protein.

There are two possibilities.

* If repressor protein *binds* to the operator then RNA polymerase is not able to bind to the promoter.

  * As a result mRNA is not transcribed by the structural genes.
  * As a result the polypeptide products of the operon are not synthesized.

* If repressor protein *does not bind* to the operator then RNA polymerase is able to bind to the promoter.

  * As a result mRNA is transcribed by the structural genes.
  * As a result the polypeptide products of the operon are synthesized.

Regulating gene expression: the operon model

Transcription factors are proteins which regulate gene expression. Repressor proteins are examples. Regulation is at the level of transcription. Operons in the bacterium *Escherichia coli* illustrate the idea.

The **lac** (lactose) **operon** encodes synthesis of **beta (ß) galactosidase** and related enzymes. The enzymes catalyse the hydrolysis of lactose to glucose and galactose making the sugars available for *E. coli* to respire.

In the absence of lactose the lac operon is inactivated.

* Its regulator gene is activated and expresses repressor protein which binds to the operator.

  * As a result the operator is inactive and mRNA is unable to bind to the promoter.
  * As a result mRNA is not transcribed by the structural genes
  * As a result β galactosidase and related enzymes are not synthesized.

* The functional advantage to *E. coli* is that the bacterium conserves energy by not synthesizing enzymes unnecessarily in the absence of their substrates (lactose, glucose, and galactose).

In the presence of lactose the lac operon is activated.

* Its regulator gene is activated and expresses repressor protein to which lactose binds, inactivating it.

  * As a result the operator is active and mRNA is able to bind to the promoter.
  * As a result mRNA is transcribed by structural genes.
  * As a result β galactosidase and related enzymes are synthesized.

* The functional advantage to *E. coli* is that the enzymes which control its metabolism are available to the bacterium.

Remember that bacteria are prokaryotes. Mechanisms similar to the operon model regulating gene expression at the level of transcription occur in the cells of eukaryotes. However, the barrier of a membrane surrounding the nucleus enables regulation to take place in other ways as well.

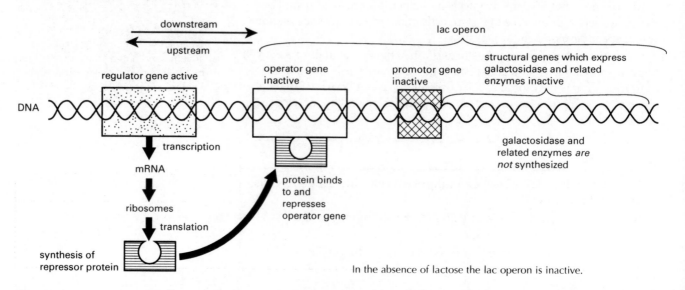

In the absence of lactose the lac operon is inactive.

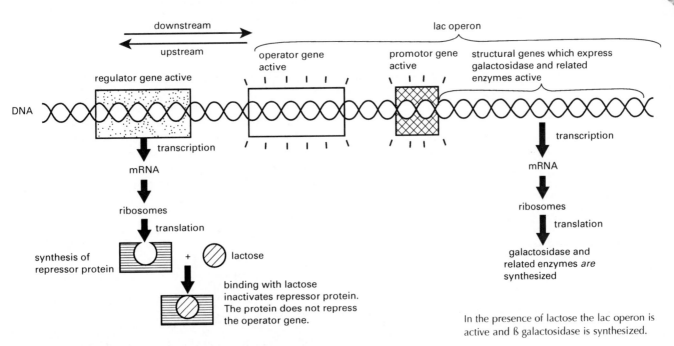

In the presence of lactose the lac operon is active and ß galactosidase is synthesized.

The effect of oestrogen on gene transcription

Oestrogen is a steroid hormone secreted into the blood by the ovaries and adrenal glands. Once in the bloodstream, oestrogen reaches most cells but acts only in those cells that have the type of protein receptor to which it can bind. The combination binds to a particular chromosomal protein and stimulates transcription of mRNA. The diagram and its checklist are your guide to the sequence of events.

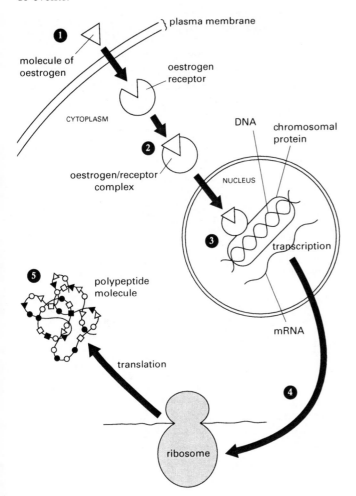

Checklist

❶ Oestrogen is lipid soluble.

    ⓡ As a result it can pass easily across the phospholipid bilayer of the plasma membrane of target cells.

❷ In the cytoplasm it binds to a receptor protein.

❸ The oestrogen/receptor complex passes from the cytoplasm through the nuclear membrane into the nucleus where it binds to a specific chromosomal protein.

    ⓡ As a result mRNA transcription begins from the DNA sequence bound to that particular chromosomal protein.

❹ The transcribed mRNA passes from the nucleus into the cytoplasm of the cell and binds with ribosomes.

❺ The mRNA is translated into polypeptide.

Oestrogen itself is not a transcription factor, but the oestrogen–receptor complex is. The cell's response to oestrogen is the altered function of the target cell as a result of newly synthesized polypeptide.

Questions

1 What are the components of an operon?

2 Explain the effect of oestrogen on its target cell.

5.23 Gene cloning technologies

OBJECTIVES

By the end of the section you should

- ○ be able to identify the technologies that allow the study and alteration of gene function
- ○ be able to describe the potential of gene therapy as an example of the application of new technologies to medical processes
- ○ be able to evaluate the effectiveness of gene therapy

Before you start it will help to read sections **5.19** (mutation), **5.21** (cystic fibrosis), **5.25** (*in vivo*), and **5.26** (*in vitro*).

Discovering gene cloning technologies

1953 James Watson and Francis Crick propose a structure for DNA.

1961 Francois Jacob and Jacques Monod propose the operon model to explain the regulation of gene expression.

1966 Francis Crick and co-workers decipher the genetic code.

1970 Enzymes are discovered which are a 'toolkit' for gene cloning technology.

- **Restriction endonucleases** (restriction enzymes) are 'molecular scissors' which catalyse reactions that cut strands of DNA into shorter lengths.

- **Ligases** catalyse the insertion (splicing) of lengths of DNA from one organism into the DNA of another different type of organism.

- **Reverse transcriptases** catalyse the synthesis of DNA from RNA.

1973 DNA is first inserted (spliced) into a **plasmid**. The technique allows genes to be cloned *in vivo*.

1977 Frederick Sanger describes the order of the bases (sequence) of the DNA of a virus called phiX174.

1983 Kary Mullis develops the **polymerase chain reaction (PCR)** which enables genes to be copied rapidly. The technique allows genes to be cloned *in vitro*.

1984 Alec Jeffreys and co-workers discover the technique of genetic **fingerprinting**.

Questions

1 What are the potential advantages of gene therapy?

2 Briefly explain the role of restriction endonucleases and ligases.

3 Explain the process of gel electrophoresis

Gene therapy

We all carry a few mutant alleles (*recall* that alleles are pairs of genes encoding a particular polypeptide). Most of them are recessive, so their possible harmful effects are masked by their normal dominant partners. However, when recessive mutations are homozygous or when the mutation is dominant, then individuals carrying them are at risk of genetic disorders. The particular disorder depends on the particular mutation.

Gene therapy aims to supplement mutant alleles with normal ones. However, the techniques are difficult, although research into long-term cures for genetic disorders is making progress.

Remember, for example, that cystic fibrosis is a genetic disorder caused by a mutant recessive allele. Healthy copies of the allele are engineered into tiny fat droplets called **liposomes**. These are carried as an aerosol spray deep into the lungs of a person affected by cystic fibrosis in an attempt to supplement the activity of the defective gene. The cells seem to take up the liposomes each with the healthy allele. However, the healthy allele must become part of the person's DNA at a locus where it is effective. Finding the right locus is just one of the difficulties of gene therapy. So far the relief of symptoms of cystic fibrosis is usually temporary. Research continues to try to make the benefits long term.

How science works (D)

The process of **electrophoresis** separates charged particles according to their molecular mass (size). For example, fragments of DNA carry a negative charge. The mixture of fragments to be separated is placed in wells at one end of a block of gel placed between two electrodes.

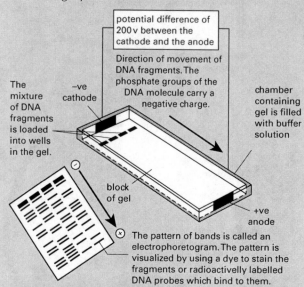

potential difference of 200 v between the cathode and the anode

Direction of movement of DNA fragments. The phosphate groups of the DNA molecule carry a negative charge.

The mixture of DNA fragments is loaded into wells in the gel.

−ve cathode

chamber containing gel is filled with buffer solution

block of gel

+ve anode

The pattern of bands is called an electrophoretogram. The pattern is visualized by using a dye to stain the fragments or radioactively labelled DNA probes which bind to them.

When the current is switched on separation of the DNA fragments begins. The fragments move through the gel towards the positive electrode. The smaller fragments move more quickly than the larger fragments and therefore travel greater distances. The different distances which the fragments move separate them into bands.

OBJECTIVES

By the end of the section you should

○ *understand that restriction endonucleases cut DNA at specific recognition sites of bases*

○ *know that ligases splice pieces of DNA into other pieces of DNA*

○ *know that reverse transcriptase converts mRNA into cDNA: the reverse of Crick's 'central dogma'*

Before you start it will help to read sections **5.18** (polypeptide synthesis), **5.23** (electrophoresis), and **5.28** (gene probes).

Different types of enzyme enable us to obtain desirable genes (the genes we want), which we can manipulate to produce substances useful to us.

Restriction endonucleases

Each of the many different restriction endonucleases is named after the bacterium in which it occurs. For example *Eco* RI comes from the bacterium *Escherichia coli*; *Hind* III from *Haemophilus influenzae*. 'One' identifies *Eco* RI as the first restriction endonuclease isolated from *E.coli*; 'three' the third restriction endonuclease isolated from *H influenzae*.

The term 'restriction enzymes' will be used to refer to restriction endonucleases from now on. The enzymes catalyse the hydrolysis of the phosphodiester bonds linking the sugar/phosphate groups of each strand of a double-stranded molecule of DNA. Each one cuts at a point following or within a particular short sequence of base pairs. The short sequence is called the **recognition site**. The recognition site is **specific** to each restriction enzyme. For example the diagram represents the recognition site for *Eco* RI.

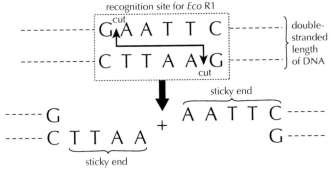

fragment 1   **fragment 2**

Notice that the recognition sequence is a palindrome... so called because the sequence GAATTC is the same as its reverse complement of bases CTTAAG.

⊕ As a result the fragments produced each have **sticky ends**.

The exposed bases of sticky ends are 'sticky' because they form hydrogen bonds with the complementary bases of the sticky ends of the fragments of other DNA molecules cut by the *same* restriction enzyme.

Not all restriction enzymes produce fragments of DNA each with sticky ends. For example, the restriction enzyme *Hpa* I cuts at the same place within its recognition site, producing **blunt-ended (flush-ended)** fragments.

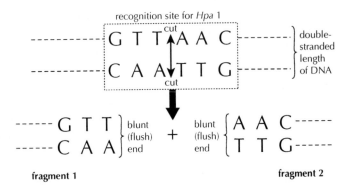

fragment 1   **fragment 2**

The lengths of DNA produced as a result of the activity of restriction enzymes form a mixture of fragments called **restriction fragment length polymorphisms** – RFLPs or 'rif-lips' for short. The fragments can be separated according to size by **gel electrophoresis**. The fragment which contains the desirable gene may be identified using a **gene probe**. Once identified, cutting out the gene containing fragments from the **gel** makes them available for transfer into the DNA of another organism.

Ligase

A gene-carrying piece of DNA can be spliced (inserted) into another piece of DNA. The pieces bond with one another. After bonding, gaps called **nicks** are left. These nicks may be sealed by adding a phosphate group. The enzyme **ligase** catalyses the reaction.

Reverse transcriptase

In 1957 Francis Crick suggested an idea he called the central dogma:

$$DNA \xrightarrow{\text{transcription}} mRNA \xrightarrow{\text{translation}} polypeptide$$

The arrows represent the transfer of information in the form of sequences of bases (DNA, mRNA) into the amino acid sequence of a polypeptide. However, the discovery that the genetic material of certain viruses is not DNA but RNA means that the central dogma does not apply in all cases. The viruses (called retroviruses, e.g. HIV) produce the enzyme **reverse transcriptase** which catalyses the conversion:

$$RNA \xrightarrow{\text{reverse transcriptase}} cDNA$$

... the reverse of the central dogma. The DNA produced is called **copy DNA (cDNA)** and does not carry sticky ends.

Questions

1 What is a recognition site?

2 What are sticky ends?

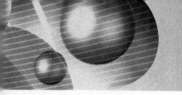

Genes can be transferred from the cells of one type of organism to the cells of almost any other type: plants → bacteria; humans → bacteria; bacteria → plants; and so on. The cells of the organism into which genes are transferred are the **host** cells and are said to be **transformed**. The organism itself is **genetically modified (GM)**.

Vectored transfer

A **vector** is a piece of DNA into which a desirable gene can be inserted. The result is a mixed (**hybrid**) molecule consisting of vector DNA and the desirable gene. The term **recombinant DNA** refers to the hybrid molecule which itself is said to be **genetically engineered**.

Inserting the desirable gene into a DNA vector is possible because of sticky ends. If the fragment of DNA containing the desirable gene is cut from the host DNA by a particular restriction enzyme which produces sticky ends, and the same restriction enzyme is used to cut the vector DNA, then the sticky ends of the gene-carrying fragment of DNA and the vector DNA are complementary and bond with one another. Ligase is used to seal the nicks (gaps) left after bonding.

Sticky ends can be added to strands of cDNA and DNA cut into blunt-ended fragments by restriction enzymes which do not produce sticky ends. Producing the sticky ends is possible by mixing the blunt-ended fragments of DNA with a mixture of nucleotides carrying the bases A T C or G and **terminal transferase**. The enzyme catalyses the addition of short single-stranded sequences of the nucleotides to each end of a blunt-ended fragment.

Bacterial plasmids are commonly used vectors. For example, a plasmid of the soil bacterium *Agrobacterium tumefasciens* induces cell division in plant tissues infected with the bacterium. Swellings called **galls** develop. Each swelling is a type of tumour. The condition is known as **crown gall disease** and the plasmid is called the **Ti (tumour inducing)** plasmid. If a desirable gene is inserted into the Ti plasmid, and a plant infected with bacteria carrying the recombinant material, the cells in the gall which develops each contain the Ti plasmid with the desirable gene in place. Multiplication of the cells in small pieces of tissue (explants) cut out of the gall produce many copies of the Ti plasmid and the desirable gene it carries – an example of **gene cloning** *in vivo*. The term *in vivo* literally means 'within the living'. We say that genes are cloned *in vivo* when they are replicated in cells dividing by mitosis.

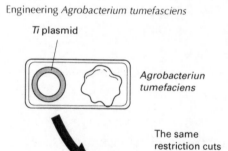

Engineering *Agrobacterium tumefasciens*

Ti plasmid

Agrobacteriun tumefaciens

The same restriction cuts open the *Ti* plasmid.

Ligase enzyme inserts the herbicide resistance gene into *Ti* plasmid.

Restriction enzyme cuts desirable gene from chromosome, e.g. the desirable gene may be a resistance gene from a chromosome of cells from a plant resistant to herbicide.

Ti plasmid with the resistance gene is put back into *Agrobacterium tumefaciens.*

Plant infected with genetically modified *A. tumefaciens* produces a crown gall. The genetic material of gall cells contains the engineered *Ti* plasmid. Explants are cut out of the gall.

Gall cells grow into plantlets.

Culture of crown gall cells, each with the engineered *Ti* plasmid as part of its genetic material.

herbicide

GM plantlets resistant to herbicide grow into mature plants.

dead weeds

Plantlets develop from explants placed in growth medium to which plant growth regulators have been added. Once transferred to soil, the plantlets grow into plants. The plants are **genetically modified (GM)** because they contain the recombinant Ti plasmid. Crops containing a herbicide-resistant gene were first produced in this way.

Vectorless transfer

Protoplasts are plant cells stripped of their cell walls. The diagram shows how protoplasts are prepared.

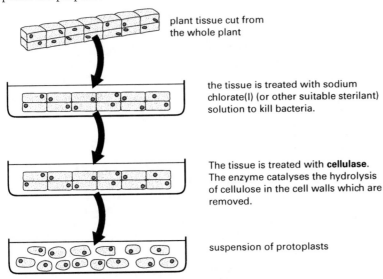

plant tissue cut from the whole plant

the tissue is treated with sodium chlorate(I) (or other suitable sterilant) solution to kill bacteria.

The tissue is treated with **cellulase**. The enzyme catalyses the hydrolysis of cellulose in the cell walls which are removed.

suspension of protoplasts

- Protoplasts will take up DNA added to the medium in which they are growing. They divide and treatment with plant growth substances stimulates the development of whole plants which carry the genes taken up by the original protoplasts.
- *Gene guns* deliver DNA directly into plant tissue. Tiny pellets of gold or tungsten coated with DNA are fired at high velocity through the walls of the cells of the tissues placed in their path. Some of the cells take up the DNA. The technique is called **biolistics**.
- *Electroporation* involves delivering bursts of electricity to cells growing in liquid containing donor DNA. The electric field creates temporary pores in the plasma membrane surrounding each cell, allowing the donor DNA to enter the cells.
- *Microinjection* involves using a syringe with a very fine glass-needle to inject DNA into the nucleus of a host cell.

In each case the transferred genes are cloned *in vivo* when the host cells divide.

How science works

Recombinant DNA and animal cloning: some issues

Some people think the benefits of recombinant DNA technology are potentially enormous; others have serious moral and ethical concerns. Here are a few points for you to think about.

Recombinant DNA technology is well established. Cloning animals from cells grown in culture is also possible. Dolly the sheep is an example. If we can clone animals like Dolly, then cloning human beings should be relatively simple (although currently illegal worldwide).

The cells which gave rise to Dolly were not transformed: they did not contain recombinant DNA. However, the technology to clone animals from transformed cells is available. Many people think that the theoretical possibility of cloning humans from transformed cells is a very dangerous idea. Others argue that such a development would make it possible to eliminate many genetic disorders.

Remember that whatever your views there are different ways of thinking about the issues raised.

How science works (I)

Why are GM crops an issue?

GM crops would seem to have real benefits. For example, growing them helps farmers to control the weeds and insect pests that damage crops and therefore reduce food production. Growing them also cuts back on the chemicals used to control the numbers of weeds and insect pests. This results is less damage to wildlife and the environment.

Why, then, are people concerned about the growing of GM crops? Here are some points to think about:

- People are worried that eating GM food may harm their health.
- There are concerns that GM crops harm wildlife.
- Pollen from crops genetically modified to resist herbicides may transfer to wild plants. If these plants are weeds, there is a danger of the development of weeds resistant to herbicides.
- Some people think that transferring genes between organisms in the laboratory is somehow 'not natural'.
- Developing countries are less easily able to afford the science needed to develop GM crops. However many of them are countries most likely to benefit from the technology. Biotech companies in developed countries can exploit the demand and dominate global markets in places least able to buy in the benefits. Anti-globalization activists believe it wrong that developed countries can dominate markets because of their financial muscle.

Remember that whatever your views, there are different ways of thinking about the issues raised.

Questions

1 Why is recombinant DNA said to be a hybrid molecule?

2 Summarize the arguments for and against GM crops.

3 Explain how the vectorless transfer of genes into host cells is possible.

4 Why might cloning mammals be controversial?

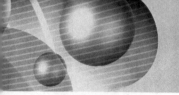

OBJECTIVES

By the end of the section you should

○ *know that the polymerase chain reaction (PCR) is used to form multiple copies of (a clone) DNA fragments*

○ *know that PCR is performed* in vitro

○ *understand the relative advantages of* in vivo *and in vitro* cloning

Before you start it will help to read section **5.25** (*in vivo* cloning).

Forming multiple copies of DNA fragments is possible using the **polymerase chain reaction (PCR)**. The DNA is cloned: we say that it is **amplified**.

Any fragment of DNA, including genes, may be cloned using PCR. Millions of copies of a DNA fragment can be synthesized in a few hours. The cloning process does not involve living cells. It is performed in labware. We refer to the technique as *in vitro* cloning.

The term *in vitro* literally means 'within the glass'. However, cloning genes *in vitro*, for example, is not necessarily performed in test tubes. The process may be contained in Petri dishes.

PCR is widely used in biological and medical research. For example, it can be used to determine evolutionary relationships between organisms, and speed up the diagnosis of infectious diseases, genetic disorders, and different types of cancer.

Often only traces of DNA evidence are found at the scene of a crime. However, amplifying the DNA collected using PCR makes enough material available for analysis.

The polymerase chain reaction (PCR). The cycle is repeated (25 cycles generates >1 million copies of the original double-stranded DNA). Each cycle lasts about 2 minutes.

Relative advantages of *in vivo* and *in vitro* cloning

Testing drugs on animals and clinical trials which test the safety of new drugs on human volunteers are examples of *in vivo* techniques. Variables are more easily controlled *in vitro*. The relative advantages of *in vivo* and *in vitro* techniques are summarized in the table.

In vivo techniques	*In vitro* techniques
Disadvantages • DNA cloning may take several weeks • a relatively large amount of DNA is needed for cloning • high cost • only fresh DNA can be cloned successfully	**Advantages** • DNA cloning is complete in a few hours • only the minutest amount of DNA is needed for cloning • low cost • degraded DNA from fossils can also be cloned
Advantages • long sequences of DNA up to 2 Mb in size can be cloned • providing the conditions promoting cell division are maintained, the amount of DNA cloned is potentially limitless	**Disadvantages** • only short sequences of DNA can be cloned • in theory the amount of DNA cloned is limitless; however in practice less DNA is cloned

Overall, *in vitro* techniques are often simpler, cheaper, and more sensitive than techniques in *vivo*. However conditions *in vitro* do not correspond to real life conditions *in vivo*, and may produce misleading results. *In vitro* studies therefore, are usually followed up *in vivo*.

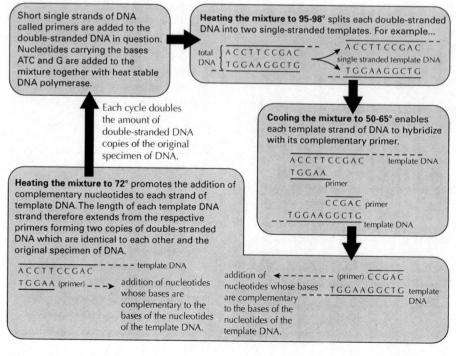

The size of DNA sequences

Gb = **giga base pairs** (1 thousand million)

Mb = **mega base pairs** (1 million)

kb = **kilo base pairs** (1 thousand)

The human genome is 3.1 Gb.

Questions

1 What is the difference between the *in vivo* and *in vitro* cloning of genes?

2 List some of the applications of PCR.

3 A genome consists of 2700 million base pairs. Which of the following units correctly describes its size?

a 2.7 kb b 2.7 Gb c 2.7 Mb

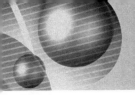
OBJECTIVES

By the end of the section you should

○ understand the use of recombinant DNA to produce transformed organisms that benefit humans using the production of insulin as an example

○ understand how transformed cells are identified

○ be able to evaluate issues associated with the use of recombinant technology

Before you start it will help to read section **5.24** (restriction enzyme, reverse transcription).

Recall that clusters of cells called the islets of Langerhans form the endocrine tissue of the pancreas. The beta (ß) cells of the islets secrete insulin. People with type I diabetes inject insulin to help regulate the concentration of glucose in their blood.

The human insulin gene can be synthesized or cut from the chromosome carrying it and inserted into a plasmid vector. The vector carries the gene into the cells of the bacterium *Escherichia coli*. The modified bacterium makes insulin. The diagram summarizes the process.

Notice:

❶ The process starts either with the mRNA encoding human insulin or the original gene. The ß cells of the Islets of Langerhans are rich in the mRNA encoding insulin, so its extraction is straight forward. The extracted mRNA is used to synthesize cDNA. The synthesis is catalysed by the enzyme reverse transcriptase.

❷ The plasmid vector carries genes encoding resistance to different antibiotics. The resistance genes are important when it comes to identifying colonies of transformed bacteria carrying the human insulin gene.

❸ Once the plasmid vector carrying the insulin gene is in place in *E.coli* cells, we say that the bacteria are genetically modified (GM). The gene continues to encode the synthesis of insulin because the genetic code works the same way in all cells.

❹ The genetically modified bacteria are put into a solution containing all of the nutrients they need for rapid replication. Replication of the bacterial cells replicates the plasmid vector and the gene it carries. The gene is cloned *in vivo*.

❺ The solution of nutrients fills huge containers called **fermenters**. The insulin produced by the bacteria is separated from the solution, purified and then packaged ready for sale (downstream processing).

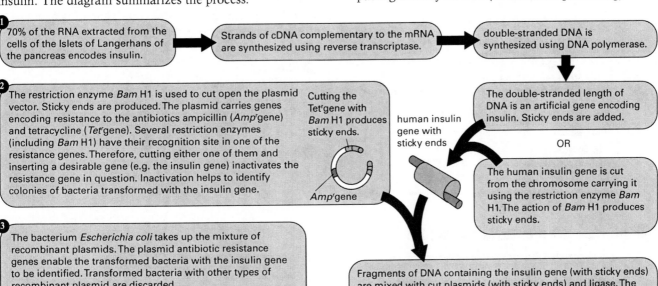

❶ 70% of the RNA extracted from the cells of the Islets of Langerhans of the pancreas encodes insulin. → Strands of cDNA complementary to the mRNA are synthesized using reverse transcriptase. → double-stranded DNA is synthesized using DNA polymerase.

❷ The restriction enzyme *Bam* H1 is used to cut open the plasmid vector. Sticky ends are produced. The plasmid carries genes encoding resistance to the antibiotics ampicillin (*Amp*ʳgene) and tetracycline (*Tet*ʳgene). Several restriction enzymes (including *Bam* H1) have their recognition site in one of the resistance genes. Therefore, cutting either one of them and inserting a desirable gene (e.g. the insulin gene) inactivates the resistance gene in question. Inactivation helps to identify colonies of bacteria transformed with the insulin gene.

Cutting the *Tet*ʳgene with *Bam* H1 produces sticky ends.

*Amp*ʳgene

human insulin gene with sticky ends

The double-stranded length of DNA is an artificial gene encoding insulin. Sticky ends are added.

OR

The human insulin gene is cut from the chromosome carrying it using the restriction enzyme *Bam* H1. The action of *Bam* H1 produces sticky ends.

❸ The bacterium *Escherichia coli* takes up the mixture of recombinant plasmids. The plasmid antibiotic resistance genes enable the transformed bacteria with the insulin gene to be identified. Transformed bacteria with other types of recombinant plasmid are discarded.

Fragments of DNA containing the insulin gene (with sticky ends) are mixed with cut plasmids (with sticky ends) and ligase. The sticky ends of the mixture combine forming recombinant plasmids which contain the insulin gene. DNA fragments *not* containing the insulin gene may also combine to form different recombinant plasmids.

✓
bacteria with recombinant plasmids containing the insulin gene

✗
bacteria with recombinant plasmids *not* containing the insulin gene

❹ Bacteria with recombinant plasmids containing the insulin gene are cultured in industrial fermenters. The plasmids replicate *in vivo* during fermentation.

nutrient solution in which bacteria replicate

❺ Insulin is produced, separated from the nutrient solution, purified and packaged ready for use to treat patients with insulin deficient diabetes.

Questions

1 Why might it be better to synthesize the human insulin gene for insertion in *E. coli* rather than isolate it from human genetic material?

2 Why does the bacterial plasmid engineered with the human insulin gene also carry genes encoding resistance to different antibiotics?

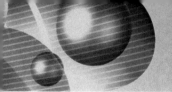

Restriction mapping

A **restriction map** shows the location of recognition sites. The base sequence of the regions of DNA between recognition sites can be worked out. Linking the regions produces the sequence of bases of the DNA molecule. The diagram and its checklist shows you how.

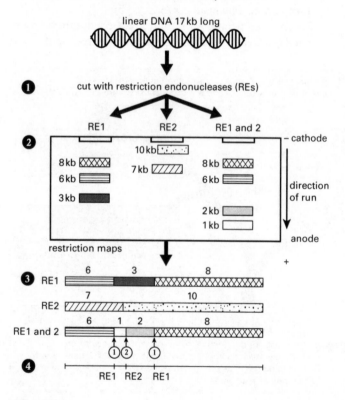

Checklist

❶ A length of DNA is cut into fragments using, in this example, two different restriction enzymes (RE1 and RE2) separately and together.

❷ The fragments of DNA are separated using gel electrophoresis.

❸ Fluorescent markers show which fragments are at each end of the original DNA. These are free ends (F). The other ends are exposed (E1 and E2) when the restriction enzymes (RE1 and RE2) cut internally

within the DNA. The possible ends of the fragments produced are:

F → E1	E1 → E1	E1→ F	
F → E2	E2 → F		
F → E1	E1 → E2	E2 → E1	E1 → F

❹ A restriction map is put together using all of the information produced. The map shows where the restriction sites 1 and 2 that correspond to the locations cut by RE1 and R2 are within the DNA.

Notice that the example illustrated is a restriction map of a sample of *linear* (length of) DNA. There are no free ends (F) to *circular* (plasmid) DNA. *Notice also* that the combined length of the fragments is equal to the original length of the DNA before it is cut with RE1 and RE2. If it were not then the fragments have not fully separated during gel electrophoresis. The reasons might be:

- partial digestion of the DNA. The cutting of the DNA into fragments using RE1 and RE2 is not complete
- fragments of similar size (although with different base sequences) might not separate and appear as one band.

DNA probes

Recall that a DNA probe is a single strand of DNA. Its base sequence is complementary to the base sequence of the gene it is designed to identify. The diagram and its checklist are your guide to the technique of using a DNA probe. The test is carried out *in vitro*.

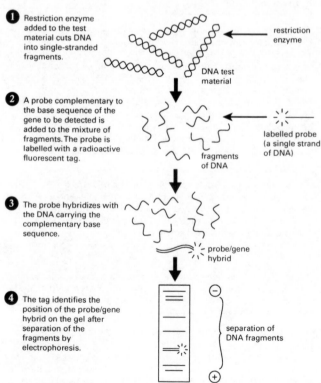

❶ Restriction enzyme added to the test material cuts DNA into single-stranded fragments.

❷ A probe complementary to the base sequence of the gene to be detected is added to the mixture of fragments. The probe is labelled with a radioactive fluorescent tag.

❸ The probe hybridizes with the DNA carrying the complementary base sequence.

❹ The tag identifies the position of the probe/gene hybrid on the gel after separation of the fragments by electrophoresis.

Questions

1 What is a restriction map?

2 Explain how a DNA probe can identify a particular gene.

OBJECTIVES

By the end of the section you should

○ *know that genetic screening uses information from DNA sequencing, restriction mapping, and DNA probes; the information is used in genetic counselling*

○ *understand why the mutated gene which encodes sickle cell anaemia is useful in one context but not in another*

Before you start it will help to read sections **4.23** (sickle cell anaemia), **5.19** (DNA sequencing), and **5.28** (restriction mapping, DNA probes).

Genetic screening uses DNA sequencing, probes, restriction mapping, and other molecular techniques to diagnose individuals who might have

- mutant genes which cause genetic disorders
- variants of genes which in combination with lifestyle increase vulnerability to particular diseases

Genetic counselling enables individuals to understand the potential benefits and limitations of screening before giving permission for testing. **Informed consent** refers to permission which is the result of advice from an expert... in the case of genetic counselling, a medical genetics expert.

Information obtained from screening is also used in the case of genetic counselling to discuss with individuals

- the basic features of any genetic disorder/gene-linked disease
- the probability of developing the disorder/gene-linked disease
- the probability of children inheriting the disorder/gene-linked disease
- the options available to manage, prevent or reduce the effects of the disorder/gene-linked disease

For example, such information enables potential parents who are both carriers of defective genes to assess the likelihood of any children inheriting both recessive alleles and therefore developing a genetic disorder. In the case of oncogenes, knowing which ones are present helps in deciding the best course of treatment for cancers.

The work of genetic counsellors continues to expand as new developments in gene technology become available. Counsellors are not only members of a health care team but also employed by companies that develop and carry out genetic testing.

Sickle cell haemoglobin: helpful or harmful?

A molecule of haemoglobin consists of chains of α and β polypeptide: two chains of each. The α chains are encoded by a particular gene; the β chains by another. The gene encoding the β chains is less stable than the gene encoding the α chains. It spontaneously mutates, resulting in the synthesis of abnormal haemoglobin which does not combine as readily with oxygen as normal molecules. Red blood cells that contain molecules of the abnormal haemoglobin are sickle shaped.

The mutant gene is recessive. Individuals who inherit the sickle gene from both parents are homozygous. They develop the symptoms of sickle cell anaemia and rarely survive childhood.

Sickle haemoglobin is the result of a point mutation. The table compares the codons.

	DNA codon	mRNA codon	Amino acid encoded
Normal haemoglobin	C-A-T	G-U-A	glutamate
Sickle haemoglobin	C-T-T	G-A-A	valine

Notice that glutamate is substituted by valine in each of the β polypeptide chains. The substitution alters the tertiary structure of each of the chains, reducing the ability of the haemoglobin molecule to absorb molecules of oxygen.

In Europe about 0.5% of the population carry the sickle gene. In warmer countries where the disease malaria is endemic, the figure rises to about 30%. Why?

Since the effect of the sickle gene is harmful we might expect that natural selection would eliminate it (the gene's presence in 0.5% of the European population reflects the natural rate of spontaneous mutation of the gene). However, the greater risk to human health from malaria outweighs the health risk to people living in warmer countries if they inherit just one copy (heterozygous) of the mutant gene. The condition is called **sickle cell trait**. People with a single copy of the gene show few symptoms of sickle cell disease, but have increased resistance to malaria. In this case the mutation is beneficial. It promotes survival! Curiously, people suffering from sickle cell anaemia are however more vulnerable to malaria – they carry two copies of the mutant gene (homozygous). In this case the mutation is harmful.

Questions

1 Let Cc represent the alleles of a carrier of cystic fibrosis. Explain why the carrier does not suffer from the disorder.

2 If two carriers of cystic fibrosis decide to have a child, what is the chance of their child suffering from the disorder.

3 What does 'informed consent' mean with reference to genetic counselling?

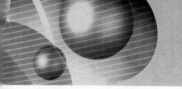

OBJECTIVES

By the end of the section you should

○ *know that an individual's DNA contains many repetitive, non-coding base sequences*

○ *know that genetic fingerprinting is used to determine genetic relationships between individuals*

○ *understand the biological principles that underpin genetic fingerprinting*

Before you start it will help to read sections **5.20** (gene expression), **5.23** (electrophoresis), **5.24** (restriction enzymes), **5.26** (PCR), and **5.28** (DNA probes).

A person's DNA is as unique as their fingerprints. Yet how can an individual's DNA be unique (except in the case of identical twins) when it is the expression of our genes that makes us all human beings? After all, the sequences of bases of the genes encoding human insulin, collagen, and the other polypeptides/proteins that build our body are usually the same for everyone. The answer is our introns – the portion of our DNA that does not encode polypeptide/proteins. Introns make up more than 97% of human DNA. Introns contain **hypervariable** regions. These have short sequences of bases each typically 5 to 10 base pairs in length. The sequences are called **core nucleotide sequences** and repeat themselves over and over again. The numbers of repeated sequences varies from individual to individual. People therefore have different lengths of hypervariable regions (the greater the number of repeats the longer the hypervariable region). Scientists noted that

- the lengths of hypervariable regions vary from person to person
- each one of us (except identical twins) has 50 to 100 types of hypervariable region different from those of other people

Noticing this was crucial to the development of **genetic fingerprinting**. Originally the term was used because the technique, like traditional fingerprinting, helps police investigate crime. The DNA of hair, blood, or other body tissues and fluids found at a crime scene is compared with DNA samples taken from suspects. The chances of the hypervariable regions of individuals (except identical twins) matching are millions-to-one. Therefore, matching genetic material from the crime scene with a suspect's DNA identifies that suspect as the likely culprit.

Fact file

Genetic fingerprinting can be used to determine the genetic relationships between individuals. For example, if there is doubt that a man or women is the parent of a particular child, then comparing the adult's genetic fingerprint with that of the child's helps to establish paternity/maternity – or not. Comparing the genetic fingerprints of individuals of a population helps to determine the genetic variability within that population.

Often only traces of DNA evidence are found at the scene of a crime. Amplifying the DNA collected using PCR makes enough material available for genetic fingerprinting. The different stages are:

Stage 1 *Extraction:* double-stranded DNA is extracted from the cells of the body fluids and/or tissues found at the crime scene.

Stage 2 *Cutting:* restriction enzymes are added to the DNA cutting it into double-stranded fragments. Some of the fragments carry hypervariable regions.

Stage 3 *Separation:* the fragments of double-stranded DNA are separated on a gel by electrophoresis. Separation produces a pattern of bands which at this stage is invisible. The double-stranded DNA is broken into single strands by immersing the block of gel in an alkaline solution.

Stage 4 *Transfer:* the single-stranded DNA fragments are transferred onto a nylon membrane. The technique is called **Southern blotting**.

Fact file

Following electrophoresis, a technique called **Southern blotting** is used to make a copy of the distribution of the separated single-stranded DNA fragments. A nylon membrane is pressed onto the electrophoresis gel. The DNA is transferred from the gel to the membrane. The pattern of positions of the DNA impregnating the membrane matches the pattern of positions of the DNA on the gel. At this stage the pattern of positions is invisible.

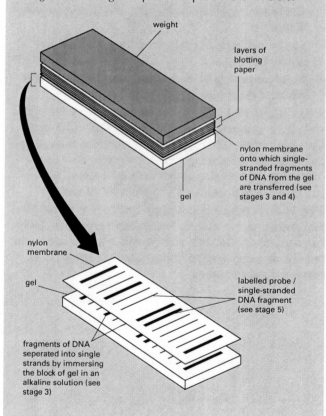

weight

layers of blotting paper

nylon membrane onto which single-stranded fragments of DNA from the gel are transferred (see stages 3 and 4)

gel

nylon membrane

gel

labelled probe / single-stranded DNA fragment (see stage 5)

fragments of DNA seperated into single strands by immersing the block of gel in an alkaline solution (see stage 3)

Stage 5 *Hybridization:* after Southern blotting the nylon membrane is immersed in a solution of DNA probes. Each probe is complementary to the core nucleotide sequence of one of the hypervariable regions carried on the DNA fragments. The probes are labelled with the enzyme **alkaline phosphatase**. In suitable conditions, the probes combine with their respective complementary DNA fragments carrying hypervariable regions with their core nucleotide sequences. Each combination is an example of a DNA hybrid (a combination of DNA strands from different sources).

Stage 6 *Display:* after hybridization the nylon membrane is covered with a phosphate containing substrate and placed over an X-ray film in the dark. The phosphatase label catalyses removal of the phosphate from the substrate. The substrate fluoresces and the X-ray film 'fogs'. When developed, the film shows a pattern of bands that looks like the bar code scanned when you buy something from a shop. The pattern identifies the position of each DNA hybrid and is the genetic fingerprint.

Stage 7 *Analysis:* the 'bar code' pattern of the fingerprint obtained from the DNA found at the crime scene is compared with the 'bar codes' of suspects. If the 'bar code' of the one of the suspects matches the 'bar code' from the crime scene, then it is likely that the person is the culprit.

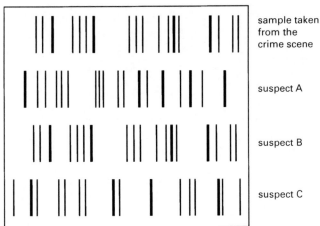

B Suspect is the most likely culprit.

How science works (K)

Qs and As

Q Why do you think a lawyer defending a suspect whose genetic fingerprint matches the fingerprint of DNA found at the crime scene might be interested to know that the DNA was contaminated with DNA from fungi before analysis?

A *Following treatment, the 'bar code' produced from the contaminated genetic material would include bands representing the DNA fragments carrying hypervariable regions of the fungi as well as of the original DNA left at the crime scene. If the contaminating bands were not present, then the 'bar code' of the DNA from the crime scene alone would not match the suspect's genetic fingerprint. The suspect therefore might not be guilty of the crime.*

Questions

1 What is the hypervariable region of an intron?
2 Summarize the different stages of genetic fingerprinting.
3 Do you think that evidence which depends on genetic fingerprinting is reliable enough to convict a suspect of a crime? Explain your answer.

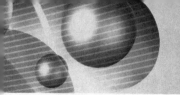
Unit 4 questions

1 The rate of photosynthesis determines the growth rate of plants. Limiting factors affect the rate of photosynthesis and therefore affect growth rate.

   a What are limiting factors?

   b Explain how a greenhouse might reduce the effects of limiting factors on the growth rate of plants.

2 Two newborn babies have been accidentally mis-assigned. The blood groups of the babies and the two sets of parents concerned have been identified.

Person	Blood group
parent **x** (father)	B
parent **x** (mother)	B
parent **y** (father)	AB
parent **y** (mother)	B
baby 1	A
baby 2	O

Alleles I^A and I^B are dominant to allele I^O but not to each other. Blood groups A and B each have two possible combinations of alleles. Which baby belongs to which set of parents?

3 Methane and carbon dioxide are sometimes called 'greenhouse' gases because they increase the greenhouse effect and therefore contribute to global warming.

   a What is the 'greenhouse' effect?

   b Explain why raising livestock and growing rice increases the amount of methane released into the atmosphere.

   c The graphs show the results of measurements taken from ice cores dating back 160 000 years.

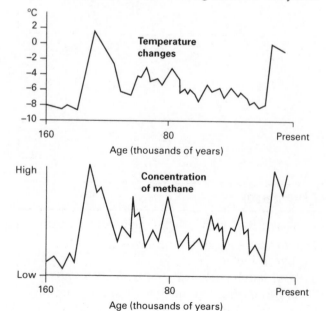

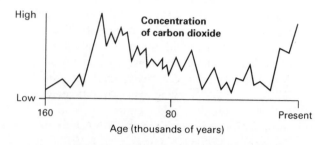

   i Comment on the reliability of the results.

   ii Do you think the results demonstrate a causal link or a correlation between the pattern of temperature change and the concentrations of carbon dioxide and methane over the last 160 years? Explain your answer.

4 Nature reserves are set up to conserve animals and plants. The effectiveness of a reserve is often determined by its size.

   a Small reserves can only support small populations of animals. Explain why small reserves limit population size.

   b Three reserves of different size were established each carrying a different number of a particular species of monkey. The amount of genetic variation in the monkeys of each reserve was measured after one, five, and ten generations of breeding. The results are shown in the table.

Number of monkeys in each reserve at the start	Percentage (%) of genetic variation after ...		
	1 generation	5 generations	10 generations
2	75.0	24.0	6.0
10	95.0	77.0	60.0
100	99.5	97.5	95.0

   i Explain the differences in the % genetic variation in the monkeys of each reserve after 10 generations of breeding.

   ii Explain why the results suggest that a large reserve would better ensure the conservation of the species of monkey than a small one.

5 The diagrams show some of the reactions which occur during photosynthesis and cellular respiration. Name the compounds labelled **w x y** and **z**.

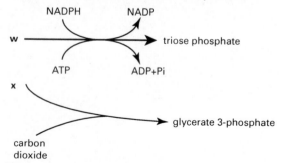

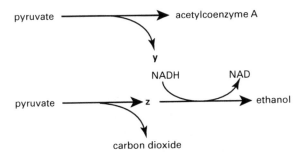

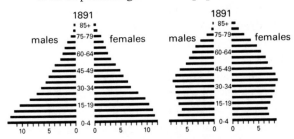

6 The pyramids show the distribution of age groups of the population of Britain for the years 1890 and 1946 as percentages of each population.

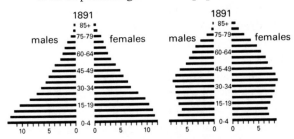

a Which pyramid indicates a rapidly increasing population? Explain your answer.

b Suggest why the shapes of the pyramids are different for the groups aged 30 and above.

7 Sampling a population showed that the percentage of the homozygous recessive genotype (aa) is 36%. Use the Hardy–Weinberg functions

$p + q = 1$

$p^2 + 2pq + q^2 = 1$

where p = the frequency of the dominant allele
            q = the frequency of the recessive allele

to calculate:

a the frequency of the 'aa' genotype

b the frequency of the 'a' allele

c the frequency of the 'A' allele

d the frequencies of the genotypes 'AA' and 'Aa'

e the frequencies of the two possible phenotypes if 'A' is completely dominant over 'a'

In each case show your working.

8 The Chi-squared (χ^2) test makes it possible to judge whether the difference between observed (O) and expected (E) values is significant. Significance is usually set at a minimum level of 95% confidence that any difference between values is real and not due to chance. We say that p = 0.05. Values of p = 0.02 and p = 0.01 means that confidence levels are 98% and 99% respectively … even better! A probability table gives the critical values for a range of probabilities. If the value of χ^2 is more than the critical value for p = 0.05 then the difference between the observed (O) and expected (E) results is significant.

The shell of the brown-lipped snail *Cepea nemoralis* exists in a number of different phenotypes (forms), varying from an unbanded yellow to a number of brown bands. The different phenotypes are determined genetically. The thrush is a predator of *Cepea*. It breaks open the shell by holding the snail in its beak and hitting the shell against a stone. In an investigation with the aim to find out whether thrushes preferred unbanded or banded snails, empty shells of *Cepea* were collected and sorted into 4 groups. The table sets out the observed results and the calculated expected results.

Group	Observed (O)	Expected (E)
broken and banded	68	63.3
broken and unbanded	30	34.7
unbroken and banded	342	346.7
unbroken and unbanded	195	190.3

Broken shells were assumed to have been predated by thrushes; unbroken shells not.

$$\chi^2 = \frac{\sum (O - E)^2}{E}$$

Where O = observed results
            E = expected results
            $\sum$ = sum of

a Complete the table. The first line has already been done for you.

Group	($O - E$)	($O - E$)^2	($O - E$)^2 / E
broken and banded	4.7	22.09	0.35
broken and unbanded			
unbroken and banded			
unbroken and unbanded	195	190.3	

b Calculate the value of χ^2, showing your working.

c An extract from a probability table for the appropriate number of degrees of freedom is shown below.

p	0.99	0.95	0.90	0.50	0.10	0.05	0.01	0.001
χ^2	0.00016	0.0039	0.016	0.46	2.71	3.84	6.63	10.83

What does your value for χ^2 suggest about the relationship between banding in *Cepaea* and predation by the thrush? Give an explanation for your answer.

9 Between 1946 and 1953 Melvin Calvin and his team at the University of California at Berkley investigated the biochemistry of photosynthesis. In particular they turned their attention to the details of the light-independent reactions. The work depended on using the radioactive isotope of carbon ^{14}C which had just become available for research work.

Calvin grew cultures of the photoautrophic protist *Chlorella* in a transparent container – the so-called 'lollipop' apparatus. Diagram 1 illustrates the set up. The *Chlorella* culture was illuminated and, with photosynthesis underway, was exposed to radioactively labelled sodium hydrogencarbonate (NaH^{14}CO$_3$). The labelled hydrogencarbonate ion (H^{14}CO$_3^-$) was fixed by the *Chlorella* to become part of the light-independent reactions. Samples of the culture were run off at regular intervals (5, 10, 15, 20 … seconds after exposure of the *Chlorella* to the radioactive isotope and the start of photosynthesis) into hot ethanol which killed the cells. The mixture was concentrated and the products of the light-independent reactions as photosynthesis got underway were separated using the recently developed technique of two-dimensional chromatography.

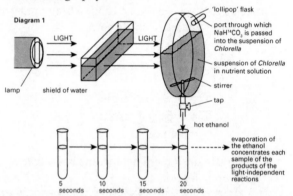

Diagram 1

Calvin reasoned that if the light-independent reactions by which carbon dioxide is reduced to make carbohydrate form a series, then by stopping the reactions at known intervals after the introduction of labelled carbon dioxide into the *Chlorella* culture, it should be possible to find the intermediate compounds in the process.

Using chromatography and autoradiography, Calvin and his co-workers traced the pathway of ^{14}C through a variety of intermediate compounds. Diagram 2 illustrates some of their results.

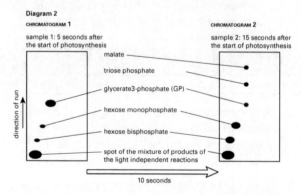

Diagram 2

a Explain the role of the radioactive isotope ^{14}C and two-dimensional chromatography in Calvin's work.

b In diagram 1, why were samples of the culture

run off from the lollipop apparatus at 5 second intervals after exposure of the *Chlorella* to the radioactive isotope and the start of photosynthesis?

c In diagram 1, explain the importance of the water shield in the experiment.

d i Describe the differences between chromatogram 1 and chromatogram 2.

  ii What do the differences suggest?

In further experiments, the light was switched off and the 'lollipop' apparatus plunged into darkness for a few seconds. Samples of *Chlorella* were taken for analysis. There was a marked

- increase in the amount of glycerate 3-phosphate (GP)
- decrease in the amount of ribulose 1,5 – bisphosphate (RuBP)

e Suggest how Calvin interpreted these results.

f With 'lights off', the synthesis of which substances stopped?

Unit 5 questions

1 The control of body temperature in humans is an example of homeostasis. The diagram summarizes the process.

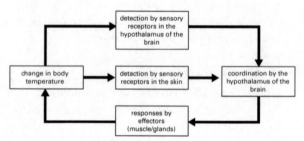

Using the diagram

a explain what is meant by the term negative feedback

b suggest how the hypothalamus coordinates the control of body temperature.

2 The diagram represents part of a myofibril of a striated muscle fibre.

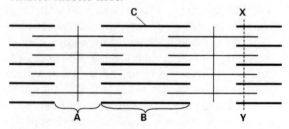

a Name the regions labelled **A** and **B**.

b Which protein makes up part C?

c Draw the appearance of a transverse section of a myofibril seen in section XY.

d Explain the role of calcium ions (Ca^{2+}) in muscle contraction.

3 The polymerase chain reaction (PCR) makes it possible to synthesize large amounts of DNA from very small samples. The diagram illustrates the process.

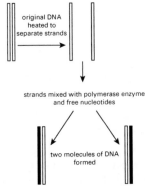

a Explain why the DNA produced in the reaction is identical to the original DNA.

b At the end of the first cycle of the reaction, there will be 2 molecules of DNA. How many molecules of DNA will there be at the end of 5 cycles?

c Why is the technique of PCR referred to as *in vitro* cloning?

4 The diagram shows some of the stages involved in the production of genetically engineered human insulin.

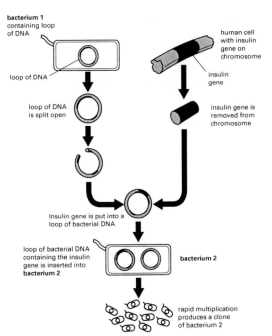

a Name the type of enzyme used to isolate the human insulin gene from its chromosome.

b Explain why the enzyme used to isolate the human insulin gene is the same as the enzyme used to split open the loop of bacterial DNA.

c Explain how the human insulin gene might be identified.

d Give a genetic explanation why rapid multiplication produced a clone of bacterium 2.

e Why is the process an example of gene cloning in vivo?

5 A piece of DNA 10 kilobases (kb) in length was

cut using the restriction enzymes *Eco*RI and *Bam*HI separately and together. The lengths of the fragments of DNA produced were as follows:

DNA	Sizes of fragments (kb)
uncut DNA	10.0
cut with *Eco*RI	8.0, 2.0
cut with *Bam*HI	5.0, 5.0
cut with *Eco*RI and *Bam*HI	5.0, 3.0, 2.0

a The diagram shows the sequence of bases where the piece of DNA is cut by *Eco*RI:

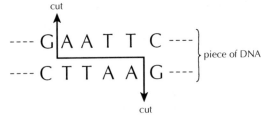

i What is the sequence of bases called?

ii The sequence is palindromic. Explain what this means.

b How many fragments are produced when the piece of DNA is cut by *Eco*RI?

c The fragments produced each have sticky ends.
  i What are sticky ends?
  ii Explain the significance of sticky ends.

d Using the data, construct a restriction map drawn to scale of the piece of DNA.

6 The diagram shows the sequence of bases on part of one strand of a DNA molecule and two mutants of the sequence:

> A A T G G C G A T
> **mutant 1** A A G G C G A T
> **mutant 2** A A T G G T G A T

a What is the name of the type of gene mutation in mutant 1 and mutant 2?

b Explain how each mutation will alter the part of the polypeptide for which this piece of DNA codes.

7 The flow chart shows the way IAA (indoleacetic acid) possibly affects cell walls.

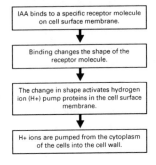

a How does the mechanism reduce the pH of the cell wall?

b How does the change in pH affect the structure of the cell wall?

c Describe two similarities between this pathway and that involved in the action of the hormone adrenaline.

8 The graph shows the changes in the permeability of an axon to sodium ions and to potassium ions during an action potential. Explain how the events shown in the graph:

a lead to the inside of the axon becoming positive with respect to the outside during the first stage of an action potential

b restore the resting potential.

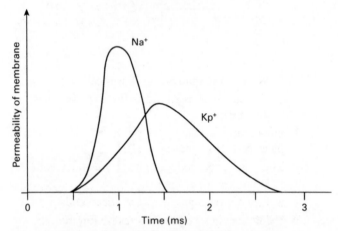

9 Genetic distance is a measure of the evolutionary relationship between species. The more distant the relationships, the greater is the genetic distance between them. DNA–DNA hybridization can be used to quantify the genetic distance between species. The technique has been used to investigate the evolutionary relationships between different species of bird.

DNA extracted from the red blood cells of two different bird species was heated, separating its strands. Single DNA strands from the different species were then combined, giving a hybrid double strand. Differences between the nucleotide sequences of the different strands weaken the bond between them. The differences mean that the temperature at which the hybrid dissociates is lower compared with pure DNA from either species. The difference in temperature at which the hybrid dissociates compared with the pure DNA is a measure of the genetic distance between the two species. The data can be used to estimate a date when the two species diverged from a common ancestor.

Using the information given and your own knowledge, answer the following questions.

a What is meant by

i genetic distance

ii common ancestor

iii species

iv nucleotide

v convergent evolution?

b Why would it not be possible to extract DNA from the red blood cells of mammals?

c Explain how

i the nucleotides of a strand of DNA are linked

ii the nucleotides of one strand of DNA are linked with the nucleotides of its partner strand.

d Why does hybrid DNA dissociate at a lower temperature than pure DNA?

e The DNA of 3 different species of bird A, B and C was extracted and hybrid DNA molecules prepared: AB and AC. Their respective dissociation temperature compared with the pure DNA of the different species was determined.

DNA	Dissociation temperature (°C)
pure A ⎤ pure B ⎬ pure C ⎦	59.5
AB	56.3
AC	57.5

i Explain how the data can be used to suggest the evolutionary relationships between the different species.

ii If 0.1°C difference in the dissociation temperature of hybrid DNA compared with pure DNA is equivalent to 1 million years before present (BP), suggest dates when species A, B and C diverged from their common ancestor.

Answers

Answers to further practice questions

Unit 4

Note to students: answers have been extended to show how you can maximize marks. [Comments are given as a further guide.]

1 a Light intensity, temperature, and supplies of carbon dioxide and water are called limiting factors because if any one of them falls below its optimum then the rate of photosynthesis slows even if the others remain optimal.

b Conditions in a greenhouse are controlled so that limiting factors are optimal. As a result the rate of photosynthesis (and therefore plant growth rate) is optimal. [To achieve maximum marks for **a** you should include '... even if the others remain optimal' as part of your answer.]

2 The genotypes of parents **x** could be either BB or BO. The genotype of parent **y** (father) can be only AB; that of parent **y** (mother) could be either BB or BO. The genotype of baby 1 could be either AA or AO; that of baby 2 can be only OO. Knowing the genotypes of parent y (father) and baby 2 and the possible genotypes of the other individuals enables you to test for the combinations that give the stated blood group of baby 1 and baby 2. [Understanding the information given is crucial to a successful answer.]

3 a The Earth's surface gives out radiant heat absorbed from the Sun. The heat is absorbed by water vapour, carbon dioxide, and other gases in the atmosphere. The gases radiate the heat back to the Earth's surface, warming it. This is the greenhouse effect.

b Bacteria ferment plant food within the gut of cattle and other livestock, producing methane. Flatulence releases the gas into the atmosphere. Bacteria living in waterlogged soil, where the concentration of oxygen is low, produce methane. The gas is released from the soil into the atmosphere.

c i Reliability depends on the strength of the proof of the relationship between changes in temperature and changes in concentration of methane and carbon dioxide in the atmosphere.

ii As the concentrations of methane and carbon dioxide rise, there is a corresponding rise in temperature. Methane and carbon dioxide are greenhouse gases. The results demonstrate a correlation between changes in temperature and concentration of the gases but not necessarily a causal link.

[You should not assume that a correlation between variables demonstrates a causal link between them. Correlation suggests that further investigation is required.]

4 a The limited amounts of available food and space limit population size.

b i The potential gene pool of the population of monkeys in each reserve is different. The smaller the population, the less genetic variation there will be in subsequent generations because of the restricted number of possible mates. This restriction in possible gene recombinations as a result of mating reduces genetic variation compared with larger populations.

ii *Any 3 of the following as part of a logical answer:* A large nature reserve is able to support a large number of monkeys. The greater the number of monkeys, the greater is the genetic variation in the population. The greater the number of monkeys, the greater the possible number of matings and therefore possible recombination of genes. The greater therefore is the genetic variation in the population from generation to generation.

[You could include an understanding of the founder effect learnt at AS as part of your answer.]

5 w = glycerate 3-phosphate (GP)

x = ribulose bisphosphate (RuBP)

y = carbon dioxide (CO_2)

z = ethanol

6 a The 1891 pyramid has the widest base/highest % of children/ greatest numbers of children (0–9 age range).

b In the 1891 pyramid the % of females is equal to the % of males, but in 1946 the % of females is greater than that of males.

In the 1891 pyramid there is a smaller % of each range compared with the 1946 pyramid.

In the 1891 pyramid there is a gradual % decrease at each age range, but in the 1946 pyramid there is a % increase at each age range from age range 15–19 to 35–39.

7 a 36%, as stated in the question.

b If the frequency of 'aa' is 36%, then $q^2 = 0.36$ and $q = 0.6$. Since q equals the frequency of 'a' then its frequency is 60%.

c Since $q = 0.6$ and $p + q = 1$, then $p = 0.4$. Since p equals the frequency of 'A', then its frequency is 40%.

d Since p^2 equals the frequency of 'AA' and 2pq the frequency of 'Aa', then the frequency of 'AA' is 16% ($p^2 = 0.4 \times 0.4 = 0.16$) and Aa is 48% ($2pq = 2 \times 0.4 \times 0.6 = 0.48$).

e Because 'A' is completely dominant over 'a', the genotypes 'AA' or 'Aa' will express the dominant phenotype. The genotype 'aa' expresses the recessive phenotype. Therefore the frequency of the dominant phenotype is equal to the sum of the frequencies of 'AA' and 'Aa', and the frequency of the recessive phenotype is the frequency of 'aa'. Therefore the frequency of the recessive phenotype is 36% (see a) and the frequency of the dominant phenotype is 64% (16% + 48% – see **d**).

8 a

Group	(O–E)	(O–E)²	(O–E)² / E
broken and banded	4.7	22.09	0.35
broken and unbanded	(–)4.7	22.09	0.64
unbroken and banded	(–)4.7	22.09	0.06(4)
unbroken and unbanded	4.7	22.09	0.12

b 0.35 + 0.64 + 0.06(4) + 0.12;

$\chi^2 = 1.17(4)$

c There is no relationship between banding in *Cepea* and predation by thrushes; or thrushes show no preference for either banded or unbanded snails because χ^2 is less than critical value at p 0.05 / less than 3.84.

Therefore the difference between observed and expected results is not significant / due to chance.

9 a Chromatography provided the means of separating the compounds extracted from the *Chlorella* culture and labelling with radioactive ¹⁴C allowed the compounds to be located on the chromatograms. Photographic film darkens where the radioactively labelled compounds are located.

b The method stopped the light-independent reactions at known time intervals after the start of photosynthesis. It was then possible to identify the main compounds present in each sample at the known time.

c Absorbs heat from the lamp.

d i During the interval of 10 seconds between running off sample 1 and sample 2 for analysis, the amounts of hexose monophosphate and hexose bisphosphate have increased while the amount of GP has decreased. Triose phosphate and malate have appeared in sample 2.

ii The changes suggest a sequence of reactions:

GP → hexose bisphosphate → triose phosphate or malate.

Unit 5

1 a Detection of a change in temperature brings about a response which corrects the change. Body temperature therefore returns to its normal value.

b The temperature regulating centre of the hypothalamus combines inputs from skin sensory receptors and from within the hypothalamus itself, bringing about the appropriate responses which controls body temperature. [Defining appropriate responses would gain additional marks – refer to the diagram on page 77.]

2 a A = I band; B = A band

b Myosin

c Refer to the diagram on page 71

d Ca^{2+} combining with troponin changes its shape, causing it and tropomyosin to move away from the myosin binding sites. As a result myosin binds with actin and muscle contraction begins.

3 a The two new strands of DNA are each the complement of the respective original DNA strand against which they form.

b 32

c 'Cloning' refers to the synthesis of multiple copies of DNA fragments identical to the original fragment. *In vitro* refers to the cloning process taking place in labware and not living cells.

4 a Restriction endonuclease/restriction enzyme

b If the human insulin gene is isolated from the host DNA by a particular restriction enzyme which produces sticky ends (*Bam*HI), and the *same* restriction enzyme is used to cut open the loop of bacterial DNA (vector DNA), then the sticky ends of the gene carrying fragment of DNA (insulin gene) and the vector DNA (loop of bacterial DNA) are complementary and bond with one another.

c Using a labelled complementary gene probe

d DNA replication and cell division produces new generations of bacterial cells genetically identical to each other and the original cells.

e The plasmid vector carrying the human insulin gene is replicated in living cells.

5 a i Recognition site

ii The sequence GAATTC is the same as its reverse complement of bases.

b 2

c i Sticky ends are 'sticky' because they form hydrogen bonds with the complementary bases of the sticky ends of the fragments of other DNA molecules cut by the same restriction enzymes.

ii Sticky ends allow a desirable gene with sticky ends to be inserted into a cut DNA vector with complementary sticky ends. The sticky ends of the desirable gene and DNA vector are complementary because each is cut at the identical recognition site using the same restriction enzyme.

6 a Mutant 1 – deletion; mutant 2 – substitution

b A deletion alters the sequence of the bases downstream of the position where the mutation takes place. This alters the sequence of bases of the section of the mRNA transcribed downstream of

the mutation, which in turn alters the sequence of amino acids translated downstream of the mutation.

A substitution also alters the sequence of bases but only within the codon affected and not downstream of it. This may change the amino acid unit encoded by the codon… or not, depending on whether the new codon is an alternative one for the same amino acid. The possibility arises because the genetic code is degenerate.

7 a It increases the concentration of H^+ in the cell wall.

b It helps to loosen the bundling of the cellulose fibres of the cell wall.

c Both IAA and adrenaline bind to their respective cell surface receptors. Binding alters the shape of the respective receptor molecule.

8 a The action of the sodium–potassium pump in the membrane of the axon stops. At 1.5 ms sodium channels in the membrane open. Sodium ions carry a positive charge (Na^+) and diffuse down their concentration gradient from the outer surface of the axon membrane to the inner surface, which therefore becomes more positive with respect to the outside.

b When the electrical potential of the inner surface of the axon membrane reaches +40 mV compared with the outer surface, its sodium channels close at 1.5 ms and potassium channels open. Potassium ions diffuse down their concentration gradient from the inner surface of the membrane to its outer surface. Diffusion continues until equilibrium is reached. Activation of the sodium–potassium pump after 2.5 ms exchanges sodium ions and potassium ions across the axon membrane, restoring the resting potential. [Including time intervals demonstrates use of the graph in answering the question.]

9 a i A measure of the dissimilarity of genetic material between different species (or individuals of the same species). A value of genetic distance can be obtained by comparing the percentage difference between the same genes or junk DNA of different species.

ii The original species from which all individuals of a particular group of organisms are directly descended.

iii A population of organisms capable of interbreeding and producing fertile offspring. [There are other definitions.]

iv Molecules that when joined together make up the structural units of DNA and RNA.

v Describes the evolution of the same characteristics (e.g. wings) in unrelated groups (e.g. insects, birds).

b The red blood cells of mammals do not contain a nucleus.

c i Through the phosphate groups forming phosphodiester bonds with the sugars deoxyribose (DNA) or ribose (RNA).

ii Hydrogen bonds between complementary bases:
A = T, C – G [– denotes hydrogen bond]

d Because hybrid DNA has a lesser degree of base pairing [due to differences in the sequence of bases of each strand of DNA forming non-complementary pairings] compared with pure DNA.

e i The lower the hybrid DNA dissociation temperature, compared with the dissociation temperature of pure DNA, the greater is the genetic distance between species. Therefore species C is more nearly related to species A than it is to species B because the difference in the dissociation temperature of the hybrid AC molecule compared with the pure DNA is less than the hybrid AB molecule.

ii Species B diverged from its common ancestor with species A and C 32 million years BP; species C diverged from its common ancestor with species A 20 million years BP.

INDEX